A Beautiful Balance

A Wellness Guide to Healthy Eating and Feeling Great

Zoë Palmer-Wright

دار جامعة حمد بن خليفة للنشر

HAMAD BIN KHALIFA UNIVERSITY PRESS

A Beautiful Balance
A Wellness Guide to Healthy Eating and Feeling Great

First published in 2019 by:
Hamad Bin Khalifa University Press
PO Box 5825
Doha, Qatar
www.hbkupress.com

ISBN: 9789927129087

....

Qatar National library cataloging in Publication Data:
A catalog record is available from (http://elibrary.qnl.
qa/iii/encore) Qatar National Library web site

Table of Contents

Gratitude

I am extremely grateful to all of the people who have helped to bring this book into being.

First and foremost, thanks to Muhammad Al Misned for providing inspiration and guidance and the support to enable me to complete the project. Without you, this book would not have been possible. Thank you for believing in this project, and in me.

Thanks to Chrissi Harcourt-Wood for your fantastic work on creative recipe development, and for all the fun in the kitchen – cooking, recipe testing and tasting! To Clare Barboza and Julie Hopper for your inspired photography and styling, which brilliantly captured just how tempting, indulgent and exciting healthy food can be.

Thanks to my inspirational mentors, Maria Saekel-Jelkmann and Dr. Siegfried Trefzer, and to my many clients and students over the years, from whom I have learnt so much.

And finally, thank you to all my loved ones: my family – Vicki, Jon, La, Milli, Dan, Max, Scarlett, Dexter and Mabel – and my wonderful friends, for your love and support.

Zoë Palmer-Wright

Foreword

My aim in this book is to show you that healthy food can taste absolutely delicious – in fact, much more delicious and satisfying than processed or fast food. Healthy food wakes up your taste buds and truly nourishes your body. You will find that once you develop a taste for eating genuinely healthy foods, the processed foods you used to enjoy will become less enjoyable and you won't want to eat them as often. It may sound unlikely to you right now, but I can honestly say that this is true. It has been my personal experience and my clients give me this feedback all the time.

It's time to stop dieting and fall in love with good food! It will make it easier for you to make better food choices and to enjoy sharing these recipes with your loved ones. I believe there is nothing better than the feeling of eating food that tastes good and is truly good for you.

Framework for Health:
The Six Pillars of Wellness

The World Health Organization's definition of health is "a state of complete physical, mental and social well-being" and not merely the absence of disease.

For me, this broader definition of health is important, as I believe that optimal wellness requires a multifaceted approach to taking care of ourselves. It involves looking after our minds and emotions, as well as our bodies.

I work with my clients in a holistic way, helping them find multiple ways to optimise their well-being. My framework for health includes six key areas to focus on improving. Each of these pillars of health is of equal importance and by paying greater attention to them, we can achieve a far higher level of well-being and happiness.

The Six Pillars of Wellness

Nutrition

Sleep

Movement

Social connection

Mindset

Meaning

Nutrition is choosing high quality, nutrient-dense foods and drinks to nourish our bodies properly and to provide the best building blocks for healthy new tissues and cells. A good diet supports optimal vitality, a balanced mood and mental wellness. It helps organs, such as our digestive system and brain, to function effectively. It helps us age better, alters the expression of our genes and provides protection against chronic disease. Over the long term, an unhealthy diet can rob us of energy and lead to obesity and chronic illnesses such as digestive disease, heart disease, cancer and type 2 diabetes.

Movement is having an active life that includes natural daily physical activities such as walking and gardening. It is exercising regularly (and in ways that support our bodies' strength and flexibility) and taking care of our posture and spinal health. Physical activity has powerful beneficial impacts on both body and mind. It builds muscles, strengthens bones and supports healthy digestion. It wards off and alleviates stress, anxiety and depression. A sedentary lifestyle is a risk factor for depression, digestive problems, cardiovascular disease, certain cancers, diabetes and obesity.

Mindset is the way we think, the skills and habits we develop that support our mental wellness and emotional health. It is about improving our relationship skills and beliefs (including building our self-esteem and self-worth, and cultivating self-compassion). It is learning healthy strategies to cope with difficult experiences and emotions. A negative mindset and poor social and emotional skills can have a serious impact on our health, can damage, or even destroy, our relationships and can limit our opportunities and experiences.

Sleep is getting enough good quality sleep to support our daytime performance, build and repair tissues, strengthen our immune system and reduce our risk of serious illness. Good quality sleep lowers blood pressure and improves memory and concentration. It has a major impact on mood, making us feel happier, more present and more calm. Chronic insomnia is linked to cardiovascular disease, diabetes and premature death. Lack of sleep can also lead to weight gain, because it alters the balance of hunger-regulating hormones, increasing appetite and cravings for fatty, sugary, carbohydrate-rich foods.

Social connection is crucial for happiness and well-being. Being part of a community and having strong social bonds strengthen the immune system and support faster recovery from disease. Social connection builds self-esteem, trust and empathy and is a determiner of longevity. Lack of social connection, isolation and loneliness have been shown to be as great a detriment to health as high blood pressure, obesity and smoking. They are drivers of anxiety, depression, addiction and suicide.

Meaning is developing a sense of purpose in life. It is about having a bigger reason to live than for yourself, a cause beyond and greater than you. It may come from faith or spirituality, but equally it may come from any other activity that feeds our soul, gives us an opportunity to connect, to serve others, to contribute to the greater good or to reflect on life's big questions. Meaning contributes to mental well-being, making us happier and more satisfied. It helps us sleep better and reduces our risk of developing heart disease and dementia.

My Food Philosophy

Food is Medicine

Our Food and the Earth

Quality Ingredients are Key

Mindful Eating

A Balanced Approach

Food is Medicine

After many years of working closely with clients, I am well aware of the huge impact that diet has on human health and how common it is for people to have multiple nutrient insufficiencies due to diets that are low in many essential nutrients.

I have found that insufficiencies of B vitamins, vitamin D, magnesium, zinc, iron, other trace minerals and omega-3 fatty acids are widespread. People are frequently overweight, but at the same time, malnourished. This is mostly due to eating a devitalised, poor-quality diet that is too low in fresh, whole plant foods and essential fats and too high in processed foods that are nutritionally depleted and laden with sugar and synthetic chemicals.

People with multiple nutrient insufficiencies usually suffer from chronic health issues as a result of their poor nutritional status. Particularly common are blood sugar issues (including diabetes), being overweight and struggling to lose weight, anxiety issues, digestive problems, constantly feeling tired, allergy symptoms, skin problems and symptoms of hormonal imbalances.

By changing my clients' diets and addressing their nutritional insufficiencies, I have witnessed first hand how these health issues can improve and sometimes be resolved entirely.

Although I work with clients on a one-to-one basis, creating individually-tailored food and wellness plans that address their unique symptoms and circumstances, I have found that there are some key dietary changes that are beneficial to all my clients, regardless of their issues.

Case Study

A man in his late twenties came to me because his chronic hay fever symptoms of sneezing, itchy eyes and runny nose were so bad that he was completely dependent on antihistamines. These drugs made him feel drowsy and groggy, but he relied on them to get through the day. His symptoms were severely impacting his productivity and ability to enjoy life.

I advised him to dramatically cut back on dairy (and to completely cut out cow's milk) as dairy products increase mucus production and often worsen hay fever, and instead focus on eating lots of fresh plant foods rich in natural antihistamines, including vitamin C-rich foods. I put him on a good quality probiotic supplement to support his immune system and on antihistamine herbal tinctures and teas.

Within two months he no longer needed to take any chemical antihistamines as he was virtually symptom free.

Case Study

A concerned mother brought her teenage daughter to me because she had persistent severe acne on her face and chest, which was undermining her confidence and self-esteem.

After looking into her eating habits, I discovered she was eating far too many processed, sugary foods and was experiencing episodes of hypoglycaemia (low blood sugar), which were disrupting her hormones. Her testosterone levels were too high, causing excess sebum production in her skin and, therefore, acne breakouts.

I put her on a diet that was low in sugar to help balance her blood sugar levels, and was full of fresh vegetables and antioxidants to provide plenty of skin-nourishing nutrients. I increased her intake of good fats (including omega-3), to calm the inflammation in her skin, and of lean protein, to provide the building blocks of healthy hormones. I also increased her intake of the mineral zinc as it is one of the most important nutrients for skin healing and removing acne scars.

Her hormone levels rebalanced, her skin became far less oily and within three months her skin had become completely clear and she had regained her self-confidence.

Our Food and the Earth

My food philosophy is built on the belief that what is good for nature and the environment is also what is best for our health. We are a part of nature and not separate from it. The Earth sustains us. By caring for the Earth, we are also caring for ourselves, our children and generations to come.

A healthier diet is also a more environmentally sustainable diet. The food you eat has a major impact both on your health and on the future of the planet. The industrialization of the food production process is a major source of greenhouse gas emissions, one of the key contributors to global warming. By changing what is on your plate, you can literally save the planet, and yourself.

" *Truly good food is both good for you and good for the environment.*"

Eco-conscious and sustainable choices

I encourage you to try to make food choices that support farming and cultivation practices that do not devastate the planet and instead help to preserve the planet and nature for generations to come. This means, wherever possible, eating more organic food and plant-based meals. It means reducing your consumption of animal products and choosing sustainable, ethically caught fish and naturally reared, free-range meat when you do eat them. It means eating more locally produced food and more whole, natural and traditionally processed foods – food that is as close to its natural state as possible.

To be clear, when I talk about processed food, I am referring to the types of food processing techniques that could be broadly described as factory or industrial processing. Industrial food processing uses sugar, processed and hydrogenated oils, white flour, synthetic food additives and high heat and pressure treatments. These techniques reduce the nutritional value of food, often rendering the finished food product hard to digest. Commercial breakfast cereals, biscuits, "diet" bars, margarine and skimmed milk are all examples of industrially processed foods.

This industrialized food processing finds its opposite in straightforward forms of artisanal food processing. Foods that have simply been chopped, soaked, cooked, fermented, dried or frozen are, in essence, processed foods but these traditional methods actually increase the digestibility of the food or help preserve it. Sauerkraut, labneh, sun-dried tomatoes, sourdough bread and lacto-fermented pickles are all examples of traditional, artisanal, processed foods that are highly nutritious. These traditional processing techniques limit nutrient losses from foods in their raw state, and in some cases, actually add to the nutritional value of the food. For example, fermenting vegetables turns them into foods full of probiotic bacteria that benefit your gut and immune health.

When comparing both industrialized food processing and artisanal food processing, the benefits to your body are mirrored by the benefits to the planet. Overall, foods that are minimally processed are less disruptive to the environment. By choosing minimally processed, sustainable foods, you are making the better choice for your health and for the environment.

Quality Ingredients are Key

Why organic?

Intensive, large scale, conventional and non-organic farming practices involve growing the same crop again and again on the same plot of land, known as monoculture, and it relies heavily on the use of synthetic chemical pesticides and fertilisers. This intensive industrial agriculture does not allow the soil to naturally replenish and is associated with decreased soil fertility, as growing only one type of plant in the same place year after year quickly depletes the nutrients in the soil that the plant relies on.

" Nutritionally - depleted soil and crops contribute to malnutrition, micronutrient deficiencies and nutritionally related disease in humans. Human health mirrors the health of the soil. "

This type of intensive farming is unsustainable. Soil nutrient depletion and soil erosion are now a worldwide problem. Overuse of synthetic pesticides and fertilisers pollutes soil and water and harms wildlife. Soil quality is directly linked to food quality, which means plants grown in nutritionally depleted soil lack the very nutrients that we, as humans, need to thrive. Nutritionally - depleted soil and crops contribute to malnutrition, micronutrient deficiencies and nutritionally related disease in humans. Human health mirrors the health of the soil. Beyond the benefits of eating more nutritious food, most of my clients also report that they find organic foods much tastier.

Non-organic crops also contain traces of synthetic pesticides and current farming methods often overuse pesticides. The safety of most synthetic pesticides is questionable and they have been connected to negative impacts on human health.

Why non-GMO?

GMOs (genetically modified organisms) are plants, animals or microorganisms that have had their genetic material (DNA) altered in a way that does not occur naturally. The aim of genetically modifying foods is to introduce a new or different characteristic to the food which is advantageous to either the producer or consumer. For example, a crop may be altered with the aim of making it more resistant to disease and insects and more tolerant to synthetic herbicides being sprayed on it, or to increase crop yield or nutritional value.

There is little scientific evidence supporting the long-term safety of genetically modified crops for human health. They raise many concerns regarding the potentially damaging effects on the environment and biodiversity. By design, many genetically modified seeds require the use of toxic synthetic pesticides, such as neonicotinoids, and some GM seeds are actually coated in a class of pesticide.

It is important to know how your food is grown or made because essentially, if it has had new genetic material, synthetic chemicals or hormones added, these products may end up in your body and adversely affect your health. Most GM food farming takes place in the U.S., Argentina, Brazil and Canada, so it can be assumed that foods from these countries are more likely to be genetically modified. Common GM food crops are: soy, corn, canola/rapeseed and maize as well as fruits and vegetables such as papaya and potatoes. Therefore, processed foods that contain these ingredients may also be contaminated.

Why eat less meat and choose free-range and organic meat?

As populations around the world grow more prosperous, people tend to change their diets to include more meat as they become more affluent. But this shift has health consequences.

A diet high in red meat increases the risk of obesity, cancer and heart disease. In addition to the negative effects that overconsumption of meat can have on your body, raising livestock generates as much carbon dioxide emissions (CO_2) as all transport (cars, trucks and automobiles) combined, which severely harms the planet. As one of the leading sources of greenhouse gases, meat production is a major cause of global warming. Cutting meat consumption to lessen the demands of raising livestock would be a big step in reducing greenhouse gases and helping tackle the problem of global warming.

On the occasions you do eat meat, choosing free-range and organic meat is the more humane and healthy choice. Factory-farmed, intensively reared animals are often kept in inhumane and cramped conditions, fed on unnatural grains rather than grass, and given antibiotics and sometimes growth hormones, which may contaminate the meat that we ultimately consume. Constant low doses of antibiotics in animal feed or water can compromise our digestive health and may also contribute to the development of drug-resistant superbugs.

Organic sources of meat ensure that livestock is kept in more natural conditions, with freedom of movement and a natural diet, free from the routine use of hormones and antibiotics, which means fewer antibiotic-resistant bacteria in the meat. These animals are able to express natural behaviours and have a higher quality of life. I encourage you to choose organic or free-range sources of meat when you do decide to eat meat; but overall, I advise limiting meat consumption in favour of plant-based meals.

Why sustainable fish and seafood?

By its simplest definition, a seafood product can be considered sustainable if it is harvested in quantities small enough to prevent population depletion and is caught in a way that does not harm other species or the marine environment. Huge numbers of fish around the world are now threatened with extinction from overfishing.

I encourage you to eat only sustainable fish whose populations are not dangerously depleted. Avoid fish that are endangered, such as hammour grouper from the Gulf and Atlantic cod, and look into which fish are available to you locally that are sustainably sourced.

Seek to eat seafood caught using methods that do not destroy the ocean environment. Avoid fish caught using bottom trawlers, which devastate the ocean bed and corals, or using methods that result in by-catch. By-catch happens when big industrial trawlers catch a specific fish or seafood such as shrimp and throw away the other types of fish (and mammals such as dolphins) caught in their nets – they are killed for absolutely no reason and discarded back into the sea.

Why less dairy?

Many people struggle to digest lactose (a sugar in dairy products) because after the age of two, humans produce less lactase, the enzyme that breaks down lactose in our digestive system. In my experience with clients, cow's milk is the most problematic type of dairy and many people find it harder to digest than sheep's, goat's or camel's milks. Cow's milk is most likely to trigger digestive, skin or respiratory problems. I have found through first-hand experience of working with clients that many people with sinus issues, asthma, acne and eczema can benefit from reducing the amount of dairy in their diet.

Another issue with dairy is modern processing techniques because of the huge difference between the digestibility of pasteurised and raw dairy products. Pasteurised dairy is exposed to high heat to kill bacteria, but this also destroys much of the nutritional content. In pasteurised milk, this particularly affects B vitamins, natural enzymes and beneficial bacteria. Destroying these nutrients makes the milk harder to digest. Good quality, organic, raw dairy products are more nutritious, digestible and better for you (as long as you are not pregnant) as they have undergone minimal processing, which means that you can benefit from the nutrients that are otherwise destroyed by the pasteurisation process. Highly processed low fat and "diet" dairy products are harder to digest than full-fat, whole dairy products and are best avoided.

I use small amounts of organic, full-fat, raw goat's or sheep's cheese in my recipes and live yoghurt and kefir as they are rich in friendly bacteria for gut health. For those who can't tolerate any dairy without getting symptoms, I also use nuts, nut milks and coconut products to get that gorgeous creamy texture in the dairy-free recipes.

Case Study

For some people, eliminating dairy can also help reduce inflammation and pain. One client was experiencing chronically painful, aching joints and her doctor suspected she had arthritis. She came to me as she wanted to see if there was anything she could do to reduce the pain without being dependent on daily painkillers.

After doing a thorough case history, and carefully assessing all the information I had gathered, the evidence suggested a possible intolerance to dairy products. I got her to try cutting dairy out of her diet completely and within three weeks she was totally pain free. I also gave her a list of calcium-rich plant foods to eat to ensure she was getting lots of calcium in her diet after eliminating dairy. In her case, the dairy had been the major trigger of the pain and inflammation in her joints.

Why less wheat and gluten?

Rates of wheat intolerance are high and rising. Many of my clients find that eating wheat makes them bloated, robs them of energy and causes abdominal discomfort, pain and constipation. They feel much better when they avoid eating wheat, or at least cut back on it.

While wheat has been at the centre of the human diet for thousands of years, changing techniques in food processing, the increase in the use of harmful pesticides, and the simple fact that we are eating a lot of refined wheat products may all be contributing to the rise in wheat intolerance.

Gluten is another culprit that can cause bloating, diarrhoea, constipation and other digestive problems such as irritable bowel syndrome (IBS), "foggy mind", depression and fatigue. Gluten is a protein found in wheat and other grains including barley and rye. Gluten sensitivity or gluten intolerance is different to coeliac disease though their symptoms are similar. Coeliac disease is a serious autoimmune disorder in which your own immune system reacts, whenever gluten is eaten, by attacking and damaging your own intestinal tissue. Coeliac disease is confirmed with a blood test. If you experience symptoms when your diet contains gluten, and those symptoms clear up when you follow a gluten-free diet, but you test negative for coeliac disease, you would be diagnosed with gluten sensitivity.

Bread and flour are staple foods and nowadays wheat cereals, cakes, pastries, pasta and pizza (usually made from refined wheat flour) make up a large proportion of many people's diets. I find that people underestimate how much wheat they are eating. They may think that they don't eat that much, but when I ask them about their diets and review their food diaries, I often find out they are having a wheat-based cereal or toast for breakfast, sandwiches or a wrap for lunch, and pasta, couscous, noodles or more bread for dinner. Wheat and gluten are also often hidden in foods we might not expect, including sauces and condiments, marinades, soups, Asian foods and meatballs.

These foods may also be contaminated with pesticides. The use of pesticides on wheat crops has increased significantly over the past 20 years and pesticide residues are regularly found on non-organic grain products. Some of these pesticides may cause gluten to become more allergenic and cause damage to our gut microbiome (essential health-promoting gut bacteria).

Our modern food processing methods may also be to blame when it comes to an increase in wheat and gluten intolerances. A few generations ago, people would have eaten mostly whole grain wheat products as opposed to the refined wheat found in today's supermarket aisles. Refined wheat products are made from wheat grain that has been processed (milled) to turn it into white flour. This means the most nutrient-packed parts of the wheat, the husk and germ, are lost along with the fibre. Removing the fibre and B vitamins makes wheat harder to digest. However, it is not this alone that causes the problems, as many people also struggle to digest whole grain wheat products.

" *Many of my clients find that eating wheat makes them bloated, robs them of energy and causes abdominal discomfort, pain and constipation.*"

It may be because we have largely abandoned traditional grain preparation methods like soaking, sprouting and fermenting. Traditional sourdough bread is made using artisanal methods from dough that has been fermented. These processes reduce hard-to-digest anti-nutrients found in grains, such as phytic acid, while naturally reducing the gluten content and making the nutrients in the grains more accessible. These methods take time (12–48 hours), so this preparation method and others like it have been abandoned in favour of faster preparation methods that allow for the quick, cheap, mass production of commercial wheat products, like loaves of bread. Many of my clients find true sourdough bread much easier to digest than those mass-produced, quickly-processed, additive-packed loaves of bread.

Although there is no definitive explanation yet as to why wheat and gluten have become less digestible and problematic for so many, it is certainly a very real phenomenon. I believe it is likely due to a combination of some of the above factors.

I recommend that you experiment yourself and see if you feel better after reducing wheat and/or gluten in your diet, and opting for whole grain and organic items when you do eat them. I encourage you to try ancient wheat varieties (like spelt, emmer or einkorn) and choose wheat products made using traditional techniques, like long-fermented (true sourdough) and sprouted breads.

Case Study

A client was experiencing chronic abdominal bloating, discomfort and constipation (her bowel movements only occurred once every other day and stools were hard and difficult to pass). She was feeling very tired and sluggish all of the time and she felt completely exhausted after eating meals. After examining her eating habits, symptoms, diet, lifestyle and medical history thoroughly, I suspected that she may be sensitive to wheat, or to some of its components, and that eating it was causing some of her symptoms. I suggested that she remove wheat from her diet and replace bread, pasta and other wheat flour products for small amounts of sourdough rye bread, brown and wild rice, quinoa, pasta made from beans, buckwheat and rice noodles, cauliflower rice and products made from tapioca, gram (chickpea) and buckwheat flour.

After following my advice, her symptoms dramatically improved within a month. She no longer felt tired all the time or like she needed to sleep after eating. Her bowel movements became regular and easier to pass. She noticed her stomach was flatter and that she felt energised both mentally and physically.

Why less refined sugar?

Refined sugar is white table sugar and other processed simple sugars that are added to foods. They may be written on a food label as high-fructose corn syrup, dextrose, maltose, glucose, sucrose or inverted cane sugar, amongst many other names.

In the refining process, natural sugar cane is stripped of its vitamins and minerals. Refined sugars show up everywhere in processed foods and they are even hidden in supposedly savoury products such as pasta sauces, salad dressings and soups. "Diet" products that are touted as low-fat are often abundant in sugar.

For most people who are in good general health and don't have allergies to any of the ingredients in these foods, there isn't anything wrong with having the occasional cake or biscuit. But eating too many products with a high sugar content is definitely a problem. Eating too much refined sugar leads to weight gain, accumulation of fat in the liver and insulin resistance, which can lead to type 2 diabetes. It also causes mood imbalances, is highly addictive, feeds bad bacteria and yeast in the gut causing bloating and other digestive issues, and can accelerate the ageing process, amongst many other problems.

I have had clients come to me saying that they often feel irritable, anxious, moody and tired and are experiencing afternoon energy slumps and occasional dizzy episodes. They are constantly craving sugar and carbohydrates and some of them have also developed adult acne and digestive bloating. In many of these cases, a thorough case history and analysis of their food diaries reveal one of the main underlying causes of their symptoms to be a diet too high in sugar and refined carbohydrates, which causes very imbalanced blood sugar levels and episodes of low blood sugar, known as hypoglycaemia. If their blood sugar issues are not addressed, they may go on to develop pre-diabetes and diabetes.

Mindful Eating

A big part of actually enjoying healthy food also comes down to how we eat. Are you always eating on the go? Do you eat standing up at the kitchen counter, at your office desk, or in front of the TV? Unconscious eating (when we are not mentally present when eating and gulp down our food too quickly) leads to overeating and weight gain.

Mindful eating on the other hand helps us to stop eating at the right time. It allows enough time for the stomach to communicate to the brain when we've eaten just enough to be satisfied, but not too full – so we can control our weight much more easily. It allows us to really taste and enjoy our food as well as being the best method of portion control.

Unconscious eating is often emotionally driven and we are far more likely to eat this way if we are stressed or upset. It can also be learnt behaviour and may be a family pattern, but it can be unlearnt.

A few tips for mindful eating:

- Take a few deep breaths before starting to eat to help you switch off from what went on before (stress, anger, etc.) and focus on the physical action of eating.

- Eat slowly. Chew your food well, taste, savour and enjoy every mouthful, putting down cutlery between mouthfuls.

- Avoid distractions such as TV while you are eating.

- Also, don't eat when emotionally upset (e.g. just after you have had an argument) and try not to eat anything in the three hours before bedtime.

- Practice portion control. Putting less on your plate will also help you to avoid eating too much in one sitting. Regularly eating oversized portions causes weight gain and is associated with diabetes.

Mindful eating is one of the best ways to control food portions and your weight. It helps us identify how foods affect us personally and to understand the links between the food we eat and our health. We are much more likely to be able to gauge whether a food causes us digestive discomfort or triggers a skin outbreak if we are paying real attention to what we are eating and how we are feeling both during and after eating different foods. We are all biochemically unique, so what works for one person won't necessarily work for you. Just because going totally gluten free worked for your friend doesn't necessarily mean it will help you. Blindly following a food philosophy or diet fad or completely eliminating multiple foods from your diet without properly evaluating how this is impacting your health and well-being can set you up for all sorts of problems.

Although I don't believe in fad diets and extreme measures to lose weight, over the years while working with clients,

I have seen first-hand that some people see very clear health improvements when they eliminate certain foods.

For example, I have seen people solve their chronic abdominal bloating by eliminating wheat; others overcome adult eczema and acne by eliminating dairy. But that doesn't mean this will work for every person with these issues as the underlying causes of these symptoms differ for each individual.

There are also certain health conditions where it is essential to avoid specific foods in order to manage symptoms and to prevent further serious harm to health. So, by all means, if you have reasons to suspect a food is causing your symptoms, experiment with eliminating it and monitor your response. Consulting a nutritionist can help you ensure that you are doing this in the correct way and that you are filling any nutritional gaps created by removing that food from your diet.

I am a firm believer in "the 80% rule" when it comes to mindful eating practices. This rule involves eating mindfully until you are 80% full. It helps with calorie restriction, which is known to extend life span and slow ageing. Okinawa, Japan, boasts some of the most fit, healthy and youthful-looking people in the world with very high life expectancy rates. They practice the 80% rule and call it Hara hachi bu. This technique means you stop eating when you feel the first sense of stomach pressure.

It can take 15–20 meals to reset the muscle memory of the stomach to get used to less food and people need to trust that it will happen. Most people are used to eating until they are full to the point of discomfort, which is way past satiation and which keeps weight on. To be clear, this is definitely not about starving yourself, going hungry, or obsessively counting calories. It is about eating until you are no longer hungry but stopping before you are uncomfortably full or "stuffed".

Ultimately, having a good diet is about being mindful about what you are eating, really listening to your body, and finding what works for you.

A Balanced Approach

Having a good diet is not about being perfect or never eating anything that isn't 100% nutritious and healthy. Obsessing about your diet and about healthy eating can be just as unhealthy as a diet full of junk food. A good diet is about eating more of the food that makes you feel good – and by good I mean energised, alive, joyful, light and calm – and eating less of the food that makes you feel sluggish, bloated, tired, anxious or depressed.

Good food is food that is rich in the nutrients that nourish you and make you healthier and stronger rather than food that makes you feel weak or unwell. Good food has the power to heal your body, support recovery from illness and help prevent disease. But too often in the battle for control over our health and weight, food becomes the enemy and guilt and anxiety become the dominant emotions connected with the food we eat and with our bodies. As we develop a love–hate relationship with food, we yo-yo between extremes of denying ourselves completely of "bad" foods and mindless bingeing on the very foods that were avoided. This vicious cycle leads to people giving themselves a hard time about what they have eaten if they binge or eat foods that are not in their diet. But the self-criticism over supposedly "bad" diet choices only makes things worse as it creates feelings of inadequacy, insecurity and powerlessness, resulting in more comfort eating or in yet another diet being started.

A good, healthy, balanced approach to food involves self-kindness and compassion. As you start this journey, I ask you first and foremost to be gentle with yourself as this will help to break unhealthy food patterns. Remember, a good diet shouldn't leave you feeling constantly hungry or unsatisfied. Food should be a pleasure and healthy eating should be enjoyable. This book does not contain a short-term diet fix; rather, it is an eating philosophy to help you change your approach to food and eating for life and gain better health and a higher quality of life.

Healthy food can taste absolutely delicious; in fact, much more delicious and satisfying than processed or fast food as it wakes up your taste buds and truly nourishes your body. As you introduce more healthy foods into your diet, and eat fewer unhealthy ones, your taste buds and your whole body will adapt and change. You will get fewer sugar cravings and, as you become more in touch with your body, some of the other unhealthy foods you used to crave and enjoy eating will no longer taste as good to you. Going forward, this will make it easier for you to eat in a healthier, more balanced way that supports your body, mind and soul and makes you feel great.

Here are my guidelines for a beautifully balanced life:

A great way to start your day is by drinking a cup of warm water with a squeeze of lemon juice, or having a cup of turmeric tea (*see p. 57*). Both wake up the digestive system and are cleansing and energising.

Eat good quality protein with each meal and try to include it in snacks as well. Good protein choices include beans and bean dips, nuts and seeds, fish, lean meat, quinoa and vegetables such as broccoli and spinach. Limit red meat to one time per week maximum, and make sure you are choosing meat from sustainable, organic sources.

Eat very few processed foods as they have been refined and stripped of their nutrients. Anything with hydrogenated oils, refined sugar and chemical additives. Artificial flavour enhancers (MSG), sweeteners (aspartame, acesulfame-k and sucralose), and synthetic colours (like tartrazine) should be consumed rarely. Overconsumption of highly processed, nutrient-deficient foods is a contributing factor to the development of diet-related chronic health issues such as obesity, type 2 diabetes, cardiovascular disease and some types of cancer.

Eat as many fresh vegetables as you can, making plant-based foods the foundation of your diet. They are packed full of health-promoting, cancer-risk reducing and anti-ageing antioxidants. Eat them raw as snacks, and dipped in hummus or other dips like baba ganoush or guacamole for extra nutrients. Add raw vegetables and fruits to breakfast, salads, side dishes, and main meals. Have them grilled, steamed and in smoothies and fresh juices. Aim for 7–10 fresh vegetables and 1–2 pieces of fresh fruit each day.

Reduce the amount of grains you eat as many people have difficulty digesting grains. Products made from refined wheat, such as white breads and pastries, are particularly problematic and frequently cause digestive problems. Overeating refined grain products also contributes to weight gain, obesity and type 2 diabetes.

Where possible, eat seasonal, local foods because foods have more nutrients when they are eaten in season. They also taste better and have less environmental impact, in terms of carbon footprint and air miles, when local.

Avoid refined sugar as much as possible. Look for refined sugars hidden in foods and drinks as they wreak havoc on blood sugar levels and negatively affect weight, health, mood and energy levels.

Eat a variety of rainbow-coloured fruit and vegetables (including their skins and outer leaves when organic) as this will help you get a wide variety of different nutrients and antioxidants in your diet. Antioxidants such as beta-carotene (in orange fruit, vegetables and green leafy vegetables), lycopene (in red tomatoes), lutein and anthocyanins (in dark red, purple and blue berries) help neutralise free radicals and subsequently will help to prevent, or at least slow down, oxidative damage to healthy cells. Without antioxidants, free radicals can cause damage to cell walls and the DNA within the cells. Over time, the ongoing effects of excessive free-radical damage and oxidative stress are linked to the ageing process and the development of many diseases, from diabetes, to cancer, to Alzheimer's.

Thirst is often mistaken for hunger, so hydrate! Skin looks younger and eyes look brighter when we are hydrated. Your individual water needs will vary depending on your health, how active you are and where you live. Tune into your body and drink whenever you feel thirsty and enjoy Skin Radiance Boosting Water throughout the day (*see p. 59*).

Eat bitter, leafy greens such as rocket, chicory, watercress, radicchio, endive, kale, and Swiss and rainbow chard; they are all packed with vitamins, minerals and fibre. Cultures around the world have traditionally eaten bitter greens to stimulate enzyme production and bile flow, which promote digestion and support natural detoxification of the liver.

Include foods that support digestive health like enzyme-rich foods such as raw vegetables, papaya, figs, pineapple, bee pollen, raw honey, raw coconut oil and raw dairy. Prebiotic foods – foods that promote probiotic bacteria in our digestive tracts – are found in asparagus, Jerusalem artichokes, leeks, onions, beans, chickpeas and lentils. Also include probiotic and fermented foods such as live yoghurt, kefir, raw apple cider vinegar, pickles, kombucha and bone broth

Eat good fats and oils as they are essential for a healthy immune system, metabolism, and the development of healthy brain and eyes. Good fats include polyunsaturated fats (such as omega-3 fatty acids), monounsaturated fats and natural saturated fats. Nuts, seeds, avocado, olives, algae, eggs and fish are all sources of healthy fats. Walnuts, chia, flax and pumpkin seeds, organic eggs, algae such as chlorella and spirulina, and oily fish such as mackerel, sardines and salmon, are all particularly good sources of omega-3 fatty acids, a type of fat that people are commonly lacking.

And finally, cook with heat-stable saturated fats such as raw coconut oil and butter from grass-fed cows and only use cold-pressed nut and seed oils (such as flaxseed, extra virgin olive or avocado oil) unheated. Use these cold-pressed oils to pour over cooked or raw food and use them as dressings, but don't cook with them. Also, check food labels to try to avoid trans fats and hydrogenated fats (in margarines and most processed foods) and steer clear of refined cooking oils sold in clear plastic bottles, such as sunflower, canola and safflower oils.

Recipes

The following recipes are influenced by my food philosophy and by my years of experience working with clients to help them enjoy the benefits of therapeutic foods. Most importantly, they reflect my true passion for food and eating well.

Without a doubt, what we eat has a major influence on both our present and future health. Learning about nutrition and changing your diet is one of the easiest and most effective ways to improve your health and the way you look and feel.

Truly good food nourishes and heals. It is one of the most powerful allies we have to enable us to live longer, healthier lives, as good nutrition is key to preventing disease and helping us to age better. Our diet plays a significant role in preventing lifestyle diseases, such as the global epidemics of type 2 diabetes and obesity, and can also help reduce the risk of developing certain cancers and heart disease.

My aim with these recipes is to give you the knowledge and practical tools to help you achieve a healthier and happier life through the food choices that you make.

So before reading on, remember:

- The key to better health is eating more real, whole, fresh, unprocessed (and traditionally processed) foods and eating less junk and fewer industrially processed and convenience foods.

- Eating more plant foods and reducing meat consumption (particularly red meat and processed meats) are essential.

- The secret to easier weight loss is not low-calorie, short-term crash diets or obsessively counting calories but mindful eating and smaller portions.

- It isn't about very low fat but instead eating the right kinds of fats, and eating less sugar, fewer grains and less dairy

- For most people, it isn't about cutting all these things out completely, but rather reducing them to get a healthier balance that works for you and your body and focusing on food quality above all else.

These recipes are packed full of vegetables, good quality proteins, vitamins, minerals, antioxidants and healthy fats.

The recipes contain no refined sugar or refined carbohydrates and are low in grain, gluten and dairy. Instead of refined sugar I use small amounts of unrefined natural sweeteners. Instead of wheat I use mostly whole, ancient grains and alternative flours. The wheat I do use is organic, whole grain and fermented and any dairy products I use are whole and organic, and contain probiotic cultures.

Enjoy experimenting and eating!

Smoothies and Drinks

Chai Matcha Latte

This spiced tea smoothie is energising, metabolism boosting, and digestion enhancing and also contains nutrients that help strengthen bones.

Antioxidant-packed matcha green tea powder provides caffeine to energise, and L-theanine to boost focus and induce calm. The cinnamon supports healthy blood sugar balance and the banana is rich in potassium, which is essential for cell hydration, regulating blood pressure and a healthy metabolic rate. Avocado provides healthy fats to keep you fuller for longer and the sesame seeds provide lots of calcium for bones. The many spices and seeds aid digestion and many people find that chia seeds can help to relieve constipation.

 ## Ingredients

■ *Serves 1*

1 tsp chia seeds
1 tbsp white sesame seeds
1 ripe banana
½ ripe avocado
½ tsp cinnamon powder
1 whole clove
2 whole cardamom pods
½ tsp ground ginger
½ tsp matcha green tea powder
1 tbsp date syrup (or 3 pitted dates)
1 ¼ cups (300ml) cashew, pistachio or almond milk

 ## To make

1. Put all ingredients other than whichever milk you are using into a blender.
2. Pour enough milk into the blender to cover all the other ingredients.
3. Blend together for 1-2 minutes, then serve.

Choco-Berry Love Potion

This yummy smoothie is one of my all-time favourites. It is full of antioxidants that help you look good while boosting endorphins in the brain that help you feel great! It is also packed with magnesium from the cacao and with vitamin C from the berries and acerola cherry.

Magnesium helps muscles relax and vitamin C has immune system-strengthening and skin collagen-boosting, anti-ageing properties. Omega-3 in the chia seeds is brain food and the raw cacao provides a number of feel-good, mood-boosting neurotransmitters. It is also packed with additional, potent anti-ageing antioxidants from the berries.

 ## Ingredients

■ *Serves 1*

1½ cups (185g) frozen mixed berries
1 tbsp chia seeds
3 tbsp raw cacao powder
1 tsp raw cacao nibs
½ ripe banana
1 tsp acerola cherry powder (or Baobab powder) – for extra vitamin C
1 cup (240ml) coconut milk (or other nut milk)
2 tsp pure date syrup (or 2 chopped pitted dates)
1 tbsp sesame seeds

 ## To make

1. Put berries, chia seeds, cacao powder and nibs, banana and cherry powder into a blender.
2. Pour enough coconut milk (or other nut milk) into the blender to cover all the other ingredients.
3. Blend for 1-2 minutes. If you have a less powerful blender, you may need to blend for a little longer.
4. Serve with a your choice of a drizzle of date syrup, chopped pitted dates, or a sprinkle of sesame seeds.

Divine Chocolate Banana Matcha

This smoothie is uplifting and energising, but calming at the same time. It also supports fat burning. Bananas are rich in potassium, an important electrolyte for regulating blood pressure and a source of tryptophan (an amino acid which is a constituent of most proteins), which is needed for the brain to make mood-lifting serotonin. The medium-chain fats in the raw coconut oil promote fat burning and protein from the almond butter keeps you full for a long time. Matcha is fat burning and contains anti-ageing antioxidants. It helps boost mental alertness and dopamine levels, yet it is also calming due to the gamma-Aminobutyric acid (GABA). The cacao also has extra mood-enhancing benefits.

 ## Ingredients

■ *Serves 1*

1 ripe banana
1 tsp organic bee pollen (only add this if you are not allergic to bees)
½ tsp matcha green tea powder
1–2 tsp date syrup (or 1-2 pitted dates)
1 tbsp raw coconut oil
3 tbsp raw cacao powder
1 tbsp raw nut butter (I use almond butter)
1 ¼ cups (300ml) coconut milk (or other nut milk)

 ## To make

1. Put all ingredients other than whichever milk you are using into a blender.
2. Pour enough coconut milk (my preference) or other nut milk into the blender to cover all the other ingredients.
3. Add a couple of ice cubes if you want it to be cold. Blend for 1–2 minutes and serve.

Creamy Vanilla Berry

This smoothie tastes like a deliciously decadent and creamy ice cream, but is completely dairy, sugar (and guilt!) free. It contains maca, raw vanilla powder, and zinc from the pumpkin seeds, to help balance hormones and support fertility. The vitamin E from the avocados, omega-3 from the flaxseed oil, beta-carotene from the lucuma fruit powder and flavonoids in the berries all help to support healthy skin, hair and nails.

 ## Ingredients

■ *Serves 1*

½ ripe avocado
1 ripe banana
1 tsp flaxseed oil
1 tsp pumpkin seeds
1 cup (108g) frozen mixed berries
1 tbsp pure vanilla powder (or 2 tsp vanilla extract)
3 tsp maca powder
1 tsp lucuma powder
1 ¼ cups (300ml) coconut or other nut milk

 ## To make

1. Put all ingredients other than whichever milk you are using into a blender.
2. Pour enough coconut milk (or other nut milk) into the blender to cover all the other ingredients.
3. Blend for 1–2 minutes and serve. This smoothie is almost as thick as a pudding. If it is too thick for you, add a big splash of nut milk to loosen.

Arabic Cardamom Cold Brew Coffee

Inspired by the deliciously spiced and aromatic Arabic coffee I have had on my travels in the Middle East, this smoothie is great before a morning workout or whenever you need to feel mentally focused, alert and energised, but without the jitteriness you can get from drinking a cup of hot coffee. This is because it is packed full of protein and good fats: omega-3 from the walnuts and medium-chain, saturated fats from the coconut oil – fats that are thought to slow the absorption of caffeine into the blood stream, resulting in a non-jittery, steady source of energy and helping to extend exercise endurance. These fats also boost brain function, provide energy and support weight loss. The coffee is made using the cold brew method and therefore is more nutritious and antioxidant rich, and the many spices, including cardamom and cloves, enhance digestion.

The night before, or some point in the three days before you want to make this smoothie, make your Cold Brew Coffee (*see p. 59*).

 ## Ingredients

■ *Serves 1*

½ ripe banana
½ ripe avocado
1 handful (15g) walnuts
⅔ cup (150ml) cold brew coffee
1 tbsp raw coconut oil
⅔ cup (150ml) nut milk (I like pistachio or coconut milk best)
1 pinch saffron threads
1 pinch cinnamon powder
¼ tsp ground clove
½ tsp ground cardamom
1 pinch nutmeg
4–5 ice cubes
To garnish: slices of banana, date syrup or coffee bean

 ## To make

1. Put all ingredients into a blender.
2. Blend for 1–2 minutes.
3. Serve over ice with a few slices of banana, a drizzle of date syrup, or a coffee bean on top.

Variations

Add 1–2 pitted dates or 1–2 tsp date syrup to sweeten.

Cold-pressed Juices

These raw, "live" vegetable and fruit juices are packed full of easy-to-assimilate nutrients to energise and hydrate.
All juice recipes make approximately 500ml – enough for either two small or one large glass of juice. Before juicing, wash vegetables and fruit well, and chop them to fit your juicer.

Immune Boost

This juice is a tropical taste sensation and a serious immunity booster. It is packed with plenty of beta-carotene, which boosts infection fighting and white blood cell production, and absolutely loads of vitamin C.

 Ingredients

1 pink grapefruit (remove skin before juicing)
½ ripe pineapple (remove skin before juicing)
5cm long (25g) piece ginger root (if the ginger is organic leave the skin on for extra nutrients)
¼ cucumber
⅓ lime (remove skin before juicing)
1 passion fruit (remove skin and cut up into pieces) and add to juice right at end – do not juice it

Skin Renew

Carrots are rich in beta-carotene, which helps enhance immunity, skin health and vision, as well as having anti-cancer properties. The chard provides plenty of skin-supporting vitamins C, K and E, and the pear and lemon provide even more of a skin radiance-enhancing and immune system strengthening vitamin C punch.

 Ingredients

5–7cm long (approx. 25g) piece turmeric root
4 carrots
½ large cucumber
¼ lemon (skin removed)
1 handful (50g) rainbow chard (or Swiss chard)
½ large pear

Super Green Detox

Packed with chlorella, kale and broccoli, this juice is full of cleansing chlorophyll (the "healing" green pigment in plants), carotenes, vitamin C and glucosinolates – detoxifying anti-cancer compounds. The broccoli is rich in the mineral chromium, a mineral which helps improve the insulin sensitivity of cells and so supports healthy blood sugar regulation.

 Ingredients

4 whole leaves of cavolo nero (black kale) (or 50g chopped kale)
½ lime (with skin left on)
2 apples
6 broccoli florets
1 cup (9g) flat leaf parsley
½ cucumber
1 tsp chlorella powder (stirred into juice well)

Turmeric Tea

A great way to start the day or energise your afternoon, this caffeine-free tea is based on a traditional Ayurvedic blend from India. It has a light, slightly peppery flavour and is naturally stimulating and anti-inflammatory. Turmeric is a potent anti-inflammatory and ginger has traditionally been used to relieve digestive symptoms such as nausea. Ginger also contains compounds with anti-inflammatory actions called gingerols that may benefit people with inflamed joints and conditions such as arthritis. Black pepper is used to help relieve digestive gas and bloating and contains piperine, a compound that helps the body absorb all the other beneficial nutrients in the tea.

 ## Ingredients

■ *Makes 4 cups (800ml)*

7.5–9.5cm long (47g) piece ginger root (skin on)
10cm long (52g) piece turmeric root (skin on)
1 pinch cayenne powder
1 pinch black pepper
½ lemon
4 cups (800ml) fresh filtered water
Optional: 1–2 tsp raw honey

 ## To make

1. Roughly chop the ginger and turmeric and add to a teapot.
2. Add the cayenne and black pepper.
3. Boil 800ml water, let cool for 1 minute and add to teapot.
4. Steep for 10–15 minutes.
5. Strain and serve with a squeeze of lemon. If you like it sweeter, add 1 tsp of raw honey.

Nut Milks

Many of my recipes use nut milks, which are a great alternative to cow's milk for dairy-sensitive people and those who struggle with health issues that can be triggered and exacerbated by dairy, such as digestive problems, sinus issues, hay fever and asthma. Nut milks can be made from virtually any nut and they all taste delicious. They are also a source of nutrients – for example, almond milk contains calcium, vitamin E and other minerals.

 ## Ingredients

■ *Makes 4 cups (800ml)*

1 cup (120g) whole raw pistachios, or cashews or almonds
7 cups (1.6l) filtered water
1 pinch cinnamon powder
1 tsp vanilla powder (or ½ tsp vanilla extract)
Optional: 1 date to sweeten

 ## To make

1. Mix the nuts and 4 cups of water in a glass jug. Stir, cover and leave in the fridge overnight.
2. In the morning, remove from the fridge and drain the soaked nuts (discarding the water).
3. Add the soaked nuts and 4 cups of fresh filtered water to a blender and blend for 60 seconds. Add cinnamon and vanilla powder (to sweeten, add a date).
4. To filter the milk, use a very fine sieve or cheesecloth. If using a sieve, place on top of a glass jug and pour the blended mixture through it (gently pressing the nut pulp in the sieve with a spatula to squeeze all the liquid out), then discard the pulp. You may want to strain again to get rid of more of the pulp.
5. Store the milk in a glass jar or covered jug in the fridge. It will keep fresh for 2–3 days.

Cold Brew Coffee

Coffee beans are rich in antioxidant polyphenols, phytochemicals with cardiovascular health benefits. The method of cold brewing the coffee (a cold extraction process) preserves the aromatic oils that provide many of the health benefits, as well as the flavour. Cold brew coffee has a sweeter, less bitter taste, is smoother and more flavoursome than coffee that has been heated. Because of its lower acidity, it is also better for your body, especially if you have a sensitive stomach or if you get heartburn. It is mellow without milk, and sweet enough without sugar.

 ## Ingredients

■ *Serves 4*

2 cups (120g) ground coffee (ideally organic and fairtrade)
2½ cups (600ml) filtered or bottled water

 ## To make

1. Add the ground coffee and water to a glass jug. Stir, cover and put in fridge for 12–24 hours (this amount of time is needed to allow the cold water to extract the coffee).
2. Remove from the fridge and filter out the coffee grounds using either a fine sieve or coffee filter paper (or even a cafetière/French Press).
3. Pour the filtered cold brew coffee into another jug.
4. You can use immediately, serve over ice or add to smoothies such as my Cold Brew Arabic Coffee Smoothie (*see p. 53*), use in baking, or cover and return to the fridge. Keep covered in the fridge for up to 2 weeks.

Skin Radiance Boosting Water

Refreshing and thirst quenching, this recipe makes it more likely that you will drink water more often, helping you to stay hydrated. Cucumber, mint and lemon infuse the water, giving additional vitamins and minerals for skin radiance. Vitamin C from the lemon and cucumber has natural anti-inflammatory properties that help prevent water retention and the silica in the cucumber promotes healthy skin and connective tissue. Make sure you are using purified or spring water to avoid the intake of chemical contaminants such as chlorine or fluoride from tap water.

The rose quartz crystal is a semi-precious stone that has traditionally been used to charge water with the positive vibrations of unconditional love, tolerance and joy.

 ## Ingredients

■ *Makes 1 large jug*

½ lemon
¼ cucumber
1 handful fresh mint leaves
7½ cups (1.5l) filtered or spring water
Optional: rose quartz crystal

 ## To make

1. Thinly slice the lemon and add to a large glass jug.
2. Using a vegetable peeler or mandoline, slice the cucumber lengthways into ribbons. Add to the jug with sprigs of fresh mint and the piece of rose quartz.
3. Add bottled or filtered water to fill the jug, then let the ingredients infuse the water. This can sit all day at either room temperature or cool in the fridge; it will taste better as the day goes on.

Breakfast

Pear and Cinnamon Pancakes

These light but satisfying pancakes are gluten, wheat and dairy free and you can make either sweet or savoury versions. They contain coconut oil, which provides medium-chain fats to support metabolism and fat burning, and gives immunity-boosting, antimicrobial properties to the pancakes. The pears are rich in fibre, vitamins C and K for healthy blood clotting and bone health, as well as a variety of antioxidant flavonoids that may help reduce the risk of type 2 diabetes.

The alternative flours from chestnut and coconut mean that they are higher in protein than pancakes made with wheat flour, which will help keep you fuller for longer. Cinnamon has been shown to have a beneficial impact on blood sugar levels.

 Ingredients

■ *Makes 12 pancakes*

1 cup (120g) tapioca flour
½ cup (80g) chestnut flour
½ cup (75g) coconut flour
2 tsp gluten-free baking powder
¾ tsp sea salt
½ tsp ground cinnamon
1 large egg
½ cup (120ml) coconut or dairy kefir (or replace with yoghurt)
1 cup (240ml) coconut milk (canned)
½ cup (120ml) nut milk (coconut or almond)
2 tbsp raw coconut oil, melted and cooled slightly
2 firm pears (Comice, Williams, Rocha)
3 tsp raw coconut oil (to grease pan between cooking each pancake)
Honey to serve

 To make

1. Sift all the dry ingredients (flours, baking powder, salt and cinnamon) together in a large bowl, making sure everything is evenly mixed.
2. In another bowl, whisk together the egg, kefir, coconut and nut milks and melted coconut oil, until combined. If you don't have kefir, all coconut milk will be fine.
3. Peel the pears and grate (avoiding the core) using the large holes of a box grater. Add the grated pears and their juices to the milk mixture.
4. Gently fold the wet ingredients into the dry and stir until everything is mixed together with no lumps. The batter mixture should be fairly thick and run slowly off a spoon – like honey. If you prefer thinner pancakes, add a little more coconut milk.
5. Heat a non-stick pan over medium heat. Add ½ tsp coconut oil and then add the batter to the pan, ¼ a cup at a time, and cook until the top starts to bubble. Check that the bottoms are golden brown and flip over to cook the other side. Cooking time is around 5 minutes.
6. Between pancakes wipe the pan clean of any stray bits of batter and add a little more (½ tsp) coconut oil.
7. Serve the pancakes hot from the pan, with a drizzle of honey. For a decadent dessert or afternoon treat, add a few crushed pecans and a dollop of coconut cream.

Savoury variations

For a delicious savoury version, try the following combinations of cold toppings (add these as toppings at the end after cooking the pancakes):

1. Place baby spinach leaves in a pan and cover with just boiled water, squeeze them dry and chop. Add 1 cup (150g) cooked chopped chicken and a pinch of grated nutmeg and parsley.
2. Use 1 cup (150g) smoked or cooked salmon torn into ribbons and mixed with 1 tbsp chopped dill and ¼ tsp mustard.
3. Grate a medium courgette and add extra salt and freshly ground black pepper, grated zest of ½ lemon, chopped fresh oregano and 1 tsp of crushed pecan nuts.

Asparagus Frittata

A satisfying breakfast to keep hunger at bay until lunchtime, this frittata helps prevent the energy dips and blood sugar crashes mid-morning that you typically get if you eat sugary commercial breakfast cereals or jam and white toast for breakfast. The frittata is packed with high quality protein, minerals and good fats – both medium-chain saturated fats in the coconut oil and omega-3 fatty acids in the eggs. The asparagus contains prebiotic fibre for digestive health and is high in the antioxidant glutathione to promote liver detoxification which helps to cleanse the blood. The spinach provides magnesium, an anti-anxiety mineral that helps muscles and the nervous system relax and iron for energy and strong, healthy hair. Nutmeg is a digestive aid and can help reduce bloating and gas and the mushrooms provide vitamin D – an essential vitamin for strong bones and a healthy immune system.

 Ingredients

■ *Serves 2*

2 tbsp raw coconut oil
1 onion, thinly sliced
1 cup (125g) mushrooms, chopped roughly
1 cup (100g) asparagus, chopped into 2.5cm pieces
6 eggs
1 tbsp coconut milk
2 cups (120g) spinach, blanched and roughly chopped
1 tbsp parsley and oregano, chopped finely
¼ tsp freshly grated nutmeg
Salt and pepper to taste

To make

1. Add half the coconut oil to a medium-sized frying pan and sauté the sliced onion, mushrooms and asparagus until tender (3–5 minutes). Remove from heat and set to one side in a bowl.
2. In a large bowl, lightly beat the eggs and coconut milk together.
3. To the egg mixture, add the blanched, chopped spinach (well squeezed to remove excess water) and the softened onions, mushrooms and asparagus. Add the parsley, oregano and nutmeg. Mix everything together until evenly distributed. Season with salt and pepper.
4. Heat the rest of the oil in the pan and pour in the frittata mixture. Cook at moderate heat until almost cooked through for about 7–10 minutes. To cook the top of the frittata, finish under the grill until the top starts to brown.
5. Transfer to a plate and cut into wedges to serve. If freezing, cool first, then cut and wrap individual wedges before bagging and freezing.

Variations

You can make this frittata with any combination of vegetables, such as:
• Mixed peppers, tomato and basil
• Kale and nutmeg
• Asparagus, salmon (smoked or plain), capers and dill
• Chicken, lemon and oregano
• Pumpkin, nutmeg and sage
• Sweet potato, feta, pine nuts and harissa-spiced roast pepper

Just make sure that you pre-cook root vegetables such as potato or pumpkin, and remove any excess moisture from water-heavy vegetables such as spinach or courgette. You can also make smaller individual portions to freeze. Bake in mini-loaf tins for about 20 minutes at 180°C, until set and springy to touch.

Harissa Baked Eggs

Eating these yummy breakfast eggs is a great way to get loads of nutrient-rich vegetables in at the start of the day. Eggs are a nutritional powerhouse; they provide B vitamins, including B12 for energy, brain function and nervous system health; the antioxidant mineral selenium, vital for thyroid health and for metabolism; and lots of good quality protein to build healthy body tissue such as hair, skin and nails.
Vitamin C and carotenoids for growth and repair of tissues, such as the skin, are found in the red and yellow peppers, and calcium, for strong hair and nails, is found in the feta and spinach. The red onion contains a decent amount of quercetin, a natural antihistamine that can help people with allergies. I have found, through working with my clients, that eating foods rich in natural antihistamines can help some people find relief from allergy symptoms. Finally, garlic is also great for immunity and digestive health.

 ## Ingredients

■ *Serves 2*

1 red onion, thinly sliced
1 red pepper, de-seeded and sliced
1 yellow pepper, de-seeded and sliced
1 tbsp raw coconut oil
½ tbsp organic butter
Salt and pepper to taste
2 garlic cloves
4 tbsp plain sheep's or goat's whole milk yoghurt (or organic Greek yoghurt)
2 tsp harissa paste or powder
1 cup (30g) baby spinach leaves
1 tbsp organic feta cheese or other soft, fresh sheep's or goat's cheese
4 eggs
To garnish: flat leaf parsley or oregano

 ## To make

1. Add the onion, red and yellow peppers to the pan, then gently fry in the coconut oil and butter until soft. Season with sea salt and a generous grinding of black pepper.
2. Crush and finely chop the garlic, add to another bowl, and mix in the yoghurt and harissa and set aside.
3. Put the spinach leaves in a colander and blanch by pouring boiling water over them until they are wilted. Squeeze any excess water out, and add to the pepper mixture in the pan.
4. Sprinkle the feta into the pan, then with the back of a tablespoon, make 4 small indents in the top of the vegetables.
5. Break an egg into each of the indents and continue to cook, or if you have an oven-proof pan, transfer it to a hot oven, around 180°C, until the egg whites are opaque and the yolk is cooked to your liking.
6. Spoon the mixture into serving bowls and add the harissa, garlic and yoghurt mixture. Garnish with a little flat leaf parsley or oregano.

Bircher Muesli with Passion Fruit and Coconut

My tropical spin on traditional European Bircher muesli is creamy and sweet with a citrus tang and can be made completely dairy free.

Oats, nuts and seeds are soaked overnight in coconut milk and lime juice. This process "activates" them by breaking down phytates and activating enzymes, which makes them much gentler on the digestive system and more digestible, so less likely to cause bloating or discomfort. The oats are also a great source of beta-glucan, a fibre that can help to lower cholesterol by helping remove bile acids via the digestive tract. Chia, sunflower and pumpkin seeds and nuts provide a mineral punch with plenty of zinc for immunity. Studies suggest the omega-3 fatty acids in the seeds may also help to improve insulin response, helping to protect against the development of type 2 diabetes. And finally, the lucuma powder, lime, apple and passion fruit mean it is packed full of the potent antioxidant vitamin C for a strong immune system and to help boost skin renewal and repair.

Ingredients

■ *Serves 4*

2 cups (170g) porridge oats
1 tbsp chia seeds
1 tbsp sunflower seeds
1 tbsp pumpkin seeds
¼ cup (30g) cashew nuts
¼ cup (20g) coconut flakes (or desiccated coconut)
2 tsp date syrup (or 2 pitted dates)
5 passion fruit
2 tsp lucuma powder
1 cup (240ml) nut milk (coconut or almond)
1 cup (240ml) water
Juice of ½ lime
1 apple
To garnish: a dollop of sheep's or coconut yoghurt

To make

1. Combine the oats, seeds, nuts, coconut flakes, date syrup, pulp of 1 passion fruit and lucuma powder in a bowl.
2. Add the coconut milk, water and lime juice and mix together.
3. Cover bowl and leave the ingredients to soak (or "activate") overnight in the fridge.
4. The next morning grate the apple into the mixture and stir. For a looser consistency, add more coconut milk.
5. Enjoy a portion of the mixture and served with a generous dollop of either coconut or sheep's yoghurt, a drizzle of date syrup and the contents of 1 passion fruit.
6. The remaining mixture can be kept in the fridge for up to 3 days.

Omelette with Feta, Rainbow Chard and Turmeric

I love this nutritious omelette for breakfast. Protein-rich eggs provide B vitamins for brain function, concentration and memory, as well as vitamin D and tryptophan to boost mood. This recipe is a great source of magnesium, vitamin K and calcium, all nutrients important for maintaining bone health. Turmeric has anti-inflammatory properties, garlic is great for immunity and the chilli will give your metabolism a kick.

The delicious rainbow chard has powerful health benefits and is incredibly good for the digestive system. It contains lots of chlorophyll, antioxidant carotenes and vitamins (including C and E) and, like other fibre-rich, leafy green vegetables, it offers protective benefits against colon cancer. Rainbow chard is also rich in biotin, which helps promote hair growth and strength.

Ingredients

■ *Serves 1*

2 leaves of rainbow or Swiss chard
1 clove garlic
½ green chilli
1cm long (approx. 5g) piece turmeric root
⅓ cup (50g) raw sheep's feta cheese (or fermented tofu if you don't eat dairy)
1 tbsp raw coconut oil
2 eggs
Sea salt and black pepper

To make

1. Finely chop the chard, garlic and green chilli and set aside.
2. Finely grate the turmeric root and set aside – use rubber gloves to prevent staining your hands.
3. Cut the feta cheese into small squares.
4. Add ½ tbsp coconut oil to a non-stick frying pan and heat on a low heat until melted, then add the chard, garlic and green chilli.
5. After 1 minute, add in the grated turmeric, then after another 1 minute, remove from heat and set to one side in a bowl.
6. Whisk the eggs in a separate bowl and add a pinch of salt and pepper.
7. Add another ½ tbsp coconut oil to the pan and heat until melted, then add the whisked eggs (swish so the egg mix covers the base of the pan) – it should start to bubble immediately. Use a spatula to lift edges away from the side of the pan and crumble the feta on top.
8. After a minute, when mostly cooked (apart from the middle), sprinkle the sautéed vegetables evenly on top. Heat for another 1 minute, then, using a spatula, fold in half and serve.

Sourdough Toast with Goat's Cheese

A super-quick breakfast for those who absolutely love cheese on toast. This healthier version is made with good quality, unpasteurised goat's cheese, which is more digestible than pasteurised cow's cheese. Proper sourdough bread made from rye or spelt makes it low in gluten and therefore much kinder to your digestive system and less likely to cause problems such as bloating than traditional cheese on white toast.

This recipe is packed with calcium for strong bones and teeth. The tomatoes provide vitamin C and the antioxidant lycopene, which may help reduce the risk of prostate cancer in men, and there is fibre and good, monounsaturated fats in the olives.

Ingredients

■ *Serves 1*

1 medium-sized ripe tomato (ideally off the vine)
4 large sweet green olives (I use the Nocellara variety)
2 slices of fresh rye or spelt sourdough bread
1 tbsp extra virgin olive oil
½ tsp raw honey
¼ cup (25g) mild goat's cheese
Sea salt and black pepper

To make

1. Finely chop the tomato and cut slivers of flesh off the olives (removing the stones). Mix the chopped tomato and olive together.
2. Lightly toast the bread.
3. In a small bowl, mix the olive oil with the honey.
4. Spread the goat's cheese on the toast, top with the tomatoes and olives and drizzle the honey and oil mix on top.
5. Finish with black pepper and a pinch of salt to taste.

Super Berry Granola

This fruity granola is for when you fancy something sweet, crunchy and nutritious for breakfast. Most supermarket granola is full of sugar and unhealthy oils, but in my version there is absolutely no refined sugar. I use coconut oil and the granola is sweetened with natural honey and cooked at a lower temperature than commercially produced cereals.

The oats are a nutritious whole grain and a great source of fibre to help keep the digestion moving. The mineral-rich nuts and seeds contain calcium for strong bones and teeth and to help maintain a regular heartbeat, and selenium, which is essential for thyroid gland function and a healthy metabolism. I like to put a couple of handfuls of the granola into a bowl with some fresh fruit, a splash of nut milk and a dollop of coconut yoghurt.

 ## Ingredients

■ *Serves 8*

5¼ cups (500g) jumbo oats
½ cup (100g) chopped Brazil nuts
½ cup (70g) sunflower seeds
½ cup (90g) sesame seeds
½ cup (170g) raw honey
5 tbsp raw coconut oil
1 tsp cinnamon powder
2 tsp vanilla pod powder (or 1 tsp vanilla extract)
2 cups (40g) freeze-dried raspberries (or goji berries)

 ## To make

1. Preheat the oven to 150°C.
2. Mix the oats, nuts and seeds in a large bowl with the honey.
3. Melt the coconut oil, over a low-medium heat, in a saucepan on the stove top and add to the bowl with the cinnamon and the vanilla. Mix together well so the nuts and oats are covered in honey and oil.
4. Line a baking tray with baking parchment and evenly scatter over the oat and nut mix.
5. Put in the oven for 15–20 minutes (until lightly golden), then remove it and give it a stir.
6. Return to the oven for 8 minutes, remove and stir again, then return for a further 8 minutes.
7. Remove from oven and leave to cool completely.
8. Mix in the freeze-dried raspberries and store the granola in an airtight glass jar. It will keep for up to 3 months.
9. Serve with nut milk, or a dollop of coconut or sheep's yoghurt, and some fresh fruit.

Lunches and Dinners

Gazpacho

Traditionally, Gazpacho is eaten cold during the summer as a cooling and hydrating soup, but it can be heated and eaten warm if you prefer.

This soup is packed with vitamins C and A (from the tomatoes, red pepper and cucumber) and a wide range of antioxidants. Tomatoes are a great source of anti-oxidants: carotenes, lycopene, zeaxanthin and lutein, which have cancer-protective effects,

support night vision, help maintain healthy mucosal surfaces of the body (such as the gut lining) and enhance skin and bone health. Cucumbers contain many phytonutrients, which are plant chemicals with disease-preventative properties, demonstrate anti-inflammatory properties, and also contain two phytonutrient compounds associated with anti-cancer benefits: lignans and cucurbitacins.

 Ingredients

■ *Serves 4*

5 cups (900g) ripe, juicy tomatoes
½ cup (120g) almonds (skin on, preferably)
2–4 garlic cloves
½ onion
1 red pepper
1 cucumber – the Lebanese variety works best
½ red chilli
½ tsp ground cumin
3 tbsp raw apple cider vinegar
1 cup (240ml) extra virgin olive oil
To garnish:
3 red radishes
½ cup (100g) mixed olives

 To make

1. Fill the kettle and boil. Rinse the tomatoes and score a cross in the top of each one. Place in a large bowl and cover with the boiling water. Leave for a few minutes.
2. Place the almonds in a separate bowl and cover with boiling water.
3. Peel the garlic and onion, and remove seeds from the pepper. Roughly chop them and the cucumber.
4. Drain the tomatoes and peel the skins – they should come away easily. Discard the skins and roughly chop the tomato flesh. Do the same for the almonds – discard the water and squeeze the nuts out of their skins.
5. Place the tomatoes, garlic, onion, pepper, cucumber, almonds and chilli in a food processor or blender. Add remaining soup ingredients and blend everything at the highest speed until completely smooth and pale. Ideally, it should be creamy with some consistency; not watery.
6. Pour into a serving bowl and add ½ cup of ice cubes, or cold water, to thin out a little.
7. Place in the fridge to chill for at least 1 hour. If needed, using ice instead of water in the previous step will speed things up.
8. Place your serving bowls in the freezer for 5 minutes to chill. Serve the soup with a sprinkle of diced radish and slivers of olives and leave the rest on the table for top-ups.

Velvet Mushroom Soup

A creamy and comforting mushroom soup that is totally lactose free, so a great option for dairy-sensitive people. I find that eating this soup in the evenings can also help you get a better night's sleep.

Mushrooms are one of the few dietary sources of vitamin D, a nutrient essential for immune function and healthy teeth and bones. You can boost the vitamin D content of the soup by leaving the mushrooms outside for half an hour in the sun before cooking – much like our skin, mushrooms transform ultraviolet light from the sun into vitamin D. Mushrooms also have polysaccharide and beta-glucan components that have anti-cancer properties. Shiitake mushrooms, in particular, have been used medicinally for thousands of years in Asia. Rich in selenium and iron, they also contain compounds with immune-strengthening actions. The addition of button mushrooms and cashews also makes the soup mineral rich, and the miso paste is a probiotic food that helps support digestion by adding to the beneficial micro-organisms of your digestive tract, and may help those with IBS and other digestive issues.

Ingredients

■ *Serves 4*

1½ small brown onions
3 tbsp raw coconut oil
2 tbsp white lentils (urid dahl) or white kidney beans (also known as haricot or cannellini beans)
¼ cup (30g) dried porcini mushrooms
1 garlic clove
1 celery stick
1 tsp ground cumin
½ tsp minced galangal
1cm long (5g) piece ginger root, cut into thin matchsticks
½ cup (60g) fresh oyster mushrooms
½ cup (60g) fresh shiitake mushrooms
½ cup (50g) fresh chestnut or button mushrooms
1 tbsp ghee or organic butter (use coconut oil if you want to avoid dairy altogether)
4 ¼ cups (1l) fresh vegetable stock (or chicken stock)
1 tsp miso paste
½ tbsp raw cashew or macadamia nut paste (you can make your own by blending raw nuts until they form a paste)
Sea salt and ground black pepper

 # To make

1. Put the lentils in a small bowl and cover with cold water to soak. In a separate bowl, cover the dried porcini mushrooms with warm water.
2. Chop the onion, garlic and celery. Place in a large heavy-based pan with 1 tbsp oil and sauté on low heat until the onions turn translucent. Place the lid on the pan to keep the moisture in whilst cooking.
3. Add the cumin, galangal and ginger to the pan and cook for 2 minutes.
4. Roughly chop all the mushrooms, including the drained porcini mushrooms, and add to the pan along with the ghee (or whatever oil you are using). Cook gently until they start to release their juices. If the pan becomes dry, add a little stock and keep the lid on.
5. Stir the miso paste into the pan, then gradually add the stock, stirring to incorporate everything.
6. Ladle a couple of tablespoons of the warm stock into a small bowl with the nut paste and blend to a smooth cream. Then add back to the pan and stir through.
7. Drain the soaked lentils and add to the pan. If using cooked white beans, add at step 9.
8. Simmer gently for about 10 minutes until the mushrooms and lentils are tender.
9. Pour into a blender and blend until smooth and creamy. Season to taste with salt and pepper.

Watercress and Avocado Soup with Coriander Salsa Verde

This cleansing and energising zesty green soup can be served either hot or cold. Onion provides plenty of collagen-boosting vitamin C for skin and hair health, as well as numerous phytochemicals – compounds that are antioxidant and anti-ageing. Onions also contain a special type of soluble fibre called fructooligosaccharide, or FOS, which promotes the growth of good bacteria in the intestines. Watercress, a bitter green leafy vegetable, helps to enhance detoxification and digestion. Celery is a brilliant source of vitamin C and coumarins, a type of phytochemical that enhances white blood cell activity and helps lower blood pressure. Celery also contains B vitamins for nervous system support and energy production. Peas are a good source of additional energising B vitamins, protein and fibre.

Avocado contains many nutrients that nourish skin and nervous system, including vitamin E. Parsley is rich in chlorophyll, vitamin C, iron and volatile oils that have been demonstrated to have anti-cancer effects.

 Ingredients

■ *Serves 4*

3 shallots (or 1 small red onion)
2 garlic cloves
2 celery sticks
2 tbsp raw coconut oil
¼ cup (30g) peas (fresh or frozen)
Zest and juice of ½ lemon
6 cups (1.5l) vegetable stock
1 tbsp finely chopped parsley
3½ cups (100g) watercress
½ tsp pink Himalayan salt
¼ tsp ground black pepper
1 ripe avocado
Coriander Salsa Verde
1 handful coriander leaves
½ red chilli
2 tsp capers
3 tbsp olive oil
½ garlic clove, crushed
Juice ½ lemon
1 tsp raw honey
Fresh black pepper

 To make

1. Roughly chop the shallots, garlic and celery. Place in a heavy-based pan with the coconut oil and sauté gently until the shallots are soft and clear.
2. Add the fresh peas, lemon zest and stock, and simmer gently for 2 minutes.
3. Wash the parsley and watercress, then roughly chop together. Add to the pan and stir well. Continue to simmer until the greens are wilted and the peas are tender.
4. Remove the pan from the heat and stir through the lemon juice, salt and pepper.
5. Scoop out the flesh of the avocado and add to the blender. Pour in the soup mixture from the pan and blend until smooth.
6. Taste to check seasoning.
7. If you want a more sophisticated, velvety soup, pass it through a sieve to remove any fibres.
8. If necessary, gently warm through again, taking care not to overheat or boil. Soup should be just warm enough, but not piping hot. Alternatively, leave to cool, then place in the fridge or freezer for a delicious chilled version.
9. To make the salsa: finely chop the coriander, chilli and capers, and place in a small serving bowl. Add all the remaining salsa verde ingredients and mix well to combine.
10. To serve, ladle the soup into bowls and drizzle some of the salsa verde on top.

Beetroot and Chicory Salad with Horseradish Goat's Curd

A detoxifying salad that also supports digestion and healthy, glowing skin – a healthy gastrointestinal tract and liver are vital for good skin. I love the way the sharp bitterness of the chicory is balanced by the creaminess of the goat's curd and the sweetness of the beetroot. The beetroot, horseradish and chicory support bile secretions, and enhance digestion and liver detoxification. Increasing bile secretion helps with the digestion of dietary fats and supports absorption of nutrients. Horseradish also has antibacterial actions and there are omega-3 fatty acids in the walnuts for brain function.

 Ingredients

■ *Serves 2 as a main meal, 4 as a starter*

4 medium-sized beetroot – red or a mixture of red and golden
1–2 tsp raw coconut oil
1 tbsp walnuts
5cm long piece of fresh horseradish root (1 heaped tbsp grated) (or
1 tsp of creamed horseradish sauce)
1 cup (250g) fresh goat's curd
1 red chicory or radicchio
2 tsp cold-pressed walnut oil (or olive oil – cold-pressed extra virgin)
2 tsp raw apple cider vinegar
Sea salt and black pepper
To garnish: 2 tsp raw honey

 To make

1. Thoroughly wash the beetroot and cut off any tough skin and the root. Rub the coconut oil over the beetroot to give a thin coating.
2. Place on a roasting tray and roast in the oven at 180°C for 40–60 minutes until tender. Check using a fork or point of a knife. If you are in a hurry, cut the beetroot into quarters before rubbing with the oil, to speed up the cooking process.
3. Put the walnuts on a separate tray and toast in the oven for 5 minutes – take care as they burn easily. Remove from the oven and crush lightly. Set aside, reserving a few for the garnish.
4. Finely grate the horseradish root and stir into the goat's curd and set aside.
5. When the beetroot is cooked, remove from the oven and leave to cool. Peel the skins and cut into quarters, then halve each quarter.
6. Toss the chicory leaves in the walnut oil and apple cider vinegar, season with salt and pepper. Arrange on a serving plate or divide between two serving plates, piling the beetroot in the centre.
7. Top the beetroot with a generous dollop of goat's curd, then garnish with the toasted walnuts and a drizzle of raw honey.
8. Serve with some delicious, warm tortillas or Gluten-Free Flatbread (*see p. 101*).

Chicory, Fennel and Apple Salad with Hot Smoked Salmon

Boost your digestion with this crisp, fresh and cleansing salad that is surprisingly satisfying and a great choice for a light lunch or dinner.

The chicory, a bitter green vegetable, and lemon juice support the digestion of the protein-rich ingredients in this dish such as the salmon. The herbs, fennel and dill have traditionally been used to help counteract digestive bloating and gas. The apple provides a group of antioxidants called polyphenols that have cardiovascular benefits and that also help to lower the rate of glucose absorption from the digestive tract. This helps to create less of an insulin spike after eating, which in turn keeps energy levels stable and means you are far less likely to get a post-meal blood sugar crash and energy slump. Studies suggest apples may also reduce the risk of asthma.

 Ingredients

■ *Serves 2*

1 large fennel bulb, bottom and stems removed and cut into very thin slices – use a mandoline or sharp knife
1 green apple, julienned (cut into matchsticks)
2 tbsp dill, finely chopped (save a few sprigs to garnish)
2 tsp lemon juice
1 tsp apple and quince molasses or pomegranate molasses (or raw honey)
2 tbsp raw apple cider vinegar
1 tbsp cold-pressed avocado oil (or extra virgin olive oil)
1 tsp raw honey
2 tbsp plain whole sheep or goat's yoghurt (for a dairy-free alternative use 1 tbsp cashew nut butter or 2 tbsp cashew nut cream[1])
Sea salt and black pepper, to taste
1 green chicory, leaves separated, rinsed and dried
1 fillet hot smoked salmon or mackerel. Cold cured salmon (such as Gravlax) or smoked salmon will also work, if you prefer them

 To make

1. Start by thinly slicing the fennel and cutting the apple into thin matchsticks. Then mix together in a large bowl with 1 tbsp of the dill.
2. Put 1 tsp lemon juice, apple and quince molasses (or honey), cider vinegar, avocado oil and honey, into a lidded jar. Add 1 tsp of warm water to loosen, secure the lid and shake to combine. Pour onto the fennel, apple and dill mixture, season with salt and pepper and toss to coat everything well.
3. In a separate bowl, mix the remaining lemon juice, honey and most of the remaining dill into the yoghurt, season with salt and pepper, and mix thoroughly.
4. Add the chicory leaves to the bowl with the fennel and apple mix and toss together.
5. Flake the smoked fish, and pile it into the centre of the salad. Drizzle the salad with the yoghurt and dill mixture and garnish with the remaining dill.

[1] *Make cashew nut cream by soaking cashew nuts for a few hours then blending into a cream.*

Seafood Salad with Mint, Lemon and Caper Dressing

A nutritious, filling salad with tons of protein from the seafood and eggs. Protein is essential for our bodies to build new tissues and healthy skin, hair and nails. The crab contains omega-3 oils, or if you prefer to use prawns or shrimps, they are a brilliant source of B12 for memory and concentration.

Courgette provides vitamin C, which is essential for skin repair and wound healing. Olive oil provides healthy monounsaturated oils and antioxidant vitamin E to nourish the skin and the apple cider vinegar and parsley have digestion-enhancing qualities.

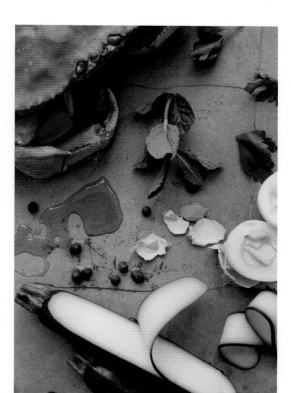

 Ingredients

■ *Serves 2*

2 eggs
1 courgette (cucumber works well too)
2 tbsp flat leaf parsley, roughly chopped
1 whole fresh cooked and prepared crab – white and brown meat
(or 1 cup [300g] of cooked prawns or shrimp)
Sea salt and black pepper
Grated zest of ½ lemon

Dressing
½ banana shallot (or onion)
1 tbsp finely chopped mint leaves
1 tsp Dijon mustard
Juice of ½ lemon
1 tsp quince and apple molasses
3 tbsp cold-pressed olive oil
2 tbsp raw apple cider vinegar
1 tsp raw honey
½ tsp pink sea salt
¼ tsp ground black pepper
2 tsp capers in brine, drained and chopped

 To make

1. Put the eggs in a pan, cover with water and bring to a boil. Cook for 6 minutes, then remove the eggs from the pan, reserving the water, and place them in a bowl of cold water. When the eggs are cool, peel and chop. Set aside in a bowl.
2. Using a vegetable peeler or mandoline, slice the courgette into ribbons. Drop the courgette ribbons into the reserved water and leave for a minute. Drain in a colander and cool under cold running water. Leave in the colander or place on paper towel to dry. Roughly chop the parsley.
3. Divide the courgette ribbons equally between two serving bowls, sprinkle over the parsley, egg and top with the crab (shrimps or prawns).
4. For the dressing: finely chop the shallot or onion. Put shallot, mint and all the remaining ingredients into a clean jar and tightly secure the lid. Shake vigorously to combine. If you don't have a jar, place in a medium bowl and whisk together until combined. Drizzle the dressing and the lemon zest over the salad and either leave as is or toss to combine everything.
5. Serve with a few slices of toasted sourdough bread, or Gluten-Free Flatbread (*see p. 101*).

Roast Chicken Recipes

These recipes use chicken thighs because although the dark meat has more saturated fat than breast meat, it is also richer in flavour and contains more minerals, such as iron and zinc, and vitamins (including B vitamins) for nervous system health. The herbs in these recipes have many health-enhancing properties – for example the recipes use antioxidant-rich thyme, which has antibacterial properties, and za'atar, an ancient blend of herbs and spices that contains many powerful antioxidants with antimicrobial effects. Prepare the chicken in advance to add to a salad or soup, put in a wrap for lunch, or serve with rice for dinner. Or try it with the Broad Bean, Fennel and Avocado Salad (see p. 94) for a lovely lunch dish.

 Ingredients

■ *Serves 2*

4 chicken thighs or 6 drumsticks
1 lemon
4 sprigs fresh thyme (or ½ tsp dried thyme)
1 tbsp raw coconut oil (or organic butter)
8 green olives
1 tsp ground coriander
1 tsp ground cumin
1 tsp ground turmeric
1 tsp za'atar
Sea salt and ground black pepper

 To make

Lemon and Thyme

1. Preheat the oven to 180°C.
2. Take the chicken thighs or drumsticks and rub all over with 1 tbsp coconut oil or butter – either rub in with your hands or melt a spoon of oil in a pan and turn the chicken around in it.
3. Place chicken in a shallow baking tray and place thyme sprigs in between the pieces.
4. Season all over with salt and pepper.
5. Roast in a preheated oven at 180°C for 30-40 minutes, depending on the size of the pieces and how many you are cooking. More pieces or larger pieces will take longer. The chicken is cooked when pierced with a knife to the bone and the juices run clear.

Lemon, Thyme and Green Olive

1. Prepare the chicken as above, using an oven-proof dish to serve.
2. Cut a lemon into wedges (1 lemon for every 6 chicken pieces) and tuck in amongst the chicken, distributing evenly. Do the same with 8 whole green, pitted olives and the thyme sprigs.
3. Drizzle with a little extra coconut oil or butter. Roast in the oven for 30-40 minutes at 180°C.

Coriander, Cumin and Turmeric

1. Preheat the oven to 180°C.
2. Place 1 tsp each of ground coriander, cumin and turmeric into a large bowl and add ¼ tsp each of salt and black pepper.
3. Add the chicken pieces to the bowl (this is enough for 6 drumsticks – make more as needed).
4. With your hands, massage the spices into the chicken pieces to coat well.
5. Melt 1 tbsp of coconut oil or butter in a shallow roasting pan, large enough to hold all the chicken with a little space in between.
6. Roll the chicken around in the oil or butter to coat evenly.
7. Roast in the oven for 30-40 minutes until juices run clear.

Za'atar

Simply coat the chicken with 1 tsp za'atar spice mix and roast in the oven at 180°C for 30-40 minutes, depending on how many pieces you are cooking and their size. More or larger pieces will take a little longer.

Grilled Chicken with Spiced Yoghurt Marinade

Chicken is a great, lean protein choice and the many herbs and spices in this recipe offer a variety of additional health benefits. Garlic is a potent infection fighter, with strong antimicrobial properties, and provides protection against heart disease through its cholesterol and blood pressure lowering effects.

Turmeric contains curcumin, a very powerful antioxidant that has been demonstrated to help protect healthy cells from free radicals, which can damage cells and lead to cancer. Turmeric also promotes liver detoxification. The ginger and capsaicin in the cayenne have digestion-enhancing effects.

 Ingredients

■ *Serves 2*

½ banana shallot (or onion)
2.5cm long (approx. 12g) piece ginger root
1 tsp ground turmeric (or 2.5cm fresh turmeric root)
1 large chicken breast (1½ cups or 250g)
5 sprigs (10g) of coriander leaves, finely chopped
3 garlic cloves
½ tsp cayenne pepper
1 tsp garam masala
¼ tsp sea salt
½ tsp black pepper
4 heaped tbsp "live" plain whole milk yoghurt
1 tbsp lemon juice

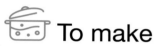 **To make**

1. Prepare this marinade either the evening before for lunch the next day, or in the morning for dinner of the same day as the chicken must marinate for at least 8 hours.

2. Start by grating the shallot (or onion), the ginger and, if using, the fresh turmeric, and cut the chicken into 1.5cm-2cm thick strips. Mix all of the herbs, spices, seasoning and lemon juice into the yoghurt, add the chicken and stir to ensure it is thoroughly coated.

3. When ready to cook, thread the chicken pieces onto two skewers, folding the strips in half to ensure they fit neatly. Lay on a plate and spoon over any remaining yoghurt marinade.

4. Heat the grill or griddle pan until hot – you can also do these on a BBQ. Place the skewers under the grill or on the griddle and cook for about 3–4 minutes each side, until they start to char on the edges and are cooked through. Check they are done by parting some of the flesh with a knife to see if they are cooked through to the centre. Rest for 5 minutes before serving.

5. These are delicious served with a simple fresh salad, such as the Sweet and Sour Slaw (see p. 111), and with Gluten-Free Flatbreads (see p. 101).

Broad Bean, Fennel and Avocado Salad with Chicken

This dish is potassium rich, metabolism boosting and high in protein due to the avocado, chicken and broad beans. Protein is essential for the body to be able to build muscle, hair and nails, and is also essential for making hormones. Broad beans are rich in fibre and many other minerals, including energising iron and calming magnesium. The avocados provide vitamin B5, which is extremely important in times of stress, and the dressing is rich in healthy oils. Deeply nourishing, when eaten as a lunch this satisfying salad helps prevent mid-afternoon energy slumps and cravings.

 Ingredients

■ *Serves 2*

1 cup (100g) fresh or frozen broad beans
½ fennel bulb
2 tsp fresh lemon juice
½ red onion
1 small ripe Hass avocado
1 tbsp mint leaves, roughly chopped
1 tbsp coriander leaves, roughly chopped
2 handfuls rocket leaves
2 roast chicken thighs and legs (4 pieces in total), shredded into strips (*see* Roast Chicken Recipes *p. 91*)
1 tbsp toasted sesame seeds

Dressing
1 tsp Dijon mustard
1 tbsp raw apple cider vinegar
2 tsp lemon juice
1 tsp raw honey
2 tbsp cold-pressed olive oil
1 tsp argan oil
Sea salt and black pepper
1 tsp pomegranate molasses or honey to serve

 To make

1. Boil the broad beans for 2–3 minutes until tender; drain and refresh under cold water. Then gently squeeze the beans out of their skins. Set aside.
2. Finely slice the fennel and place in a bowl with 2 tsp of lemon juice. Toss together and set aside – this will allow the fennel to soften a little.
3. Finely slice the onion, chop the avocado into cubes and combine together in a salad bowl with the chopped mint, coriander and rocket leaves. Add the fennel and broad beans and toss again to mix through.
4. In a separate bowl, or lidded jar, mix the dressing ingredients together. Add to the rocket, avocado and herb mix and toss gently to cover everything with the dressing.
5. Divide the salad between serving dishes to create the salad "bed". Then pile the shredded chicken on top, sprinkle with the toasted sesame seeds and drizzle with 1 tsp of pomegranate molasses (or honey) to serve.

Spicy Fish Broth with Fresh Greens

This Asian-inspired soup boosts the immune system and is nourishing and hydrating – great for warding off colds and flu. The kale, Swiss chard and broccoli provide loads of vitamins, including immunity-boosting beta-carotene, minerals and detoxifying antioxidants. The fish provides protein to help the body heal itself. The shallots, spring onions and garlic together give significant antimicrobial benefits to this dish. The presence of garlic is particularly important as it contains allicin – "nature's antibiotic". Carrots provide more beta-carotene, which helps the body produce infection-fighting cells as well as promoting good vision. Carotenes also have a protective effect against cancer development. Ginger and chilli have circulation-enhancing, warming and decongestant actions.

Ingredients

■ *Serves 2*

2 banana shallots (or 1 large onion)
3 garlic cloves, peeled
1 handful (50g) kale leaves
1 handful (50g) Swiss chard
1 medium carrot, peeled
1 handful (100g) purple sprouting broccoli, greens included (or normal broccoli)
3–4 spring onions
1.3cm long (7g) piece ginger root
½–1 fresh red chilli
1 tbsp raw coconut oil
1 ¾ cups (400ml) bone broth (lamb or beef) or good quality fish stock
1 ¾ cups (400ml) water
1 generous tsp tamarind paste
1 cup (270g) fresh salmon fillet (or sordid sweetlips/yanam), skin and bones removed
1 tsp pink Himalayan salt
Freshly ground black pepper
1 heaped tbsp coriander leaves
Juice of 1 lime
2 tsp black sesame seeds
2 tsp toasted sesame oil

 # To make

1. Prepare all the vegetables: thinly slice the shallots (or onion), crush and chop the garlic, slice the greens into 1cm strips, julienne the carrots (cut into matchstick-size pieces), cut the broccoli into equal-sized florets and slice the stems and leaves into 1cm pieces. Thinly slice the spring onions, ginger and chilli (remove the seeds before chopping).
2. Gently heat the coconut oil in a large saucepan, add the shallots and sauté gently until they start to soften, then add the garlic and continue to cook for 1–2 minutes more.
3. Add the stock and water and heat to a gentle simmer. Spoon a little of the warm stock mix in a small dish, add the tamarind and mix with a fork, then add this mixture to the pan.
4. Add the ginger and chilli and simmer for a couple of minutes, then add the rest of the vegetables. Simmer gently for 2–3 minutes.
5. Cut the fish into 2.5cm cubes and add to the pan. Season with salt (to your taste) and a good grinding of fresh black pepper.
6. Leave to simmer gently for 2 more minutes until the fish is just cooked through (take care not to overcook it). Check by pushing a piece with a fork – it should flake quite easily when prodded.
7. Roughly chop the coriander and add to the broth with the lime juice.
8. Divide the broth between 2 bowls, drizzle each bowl with 1 tsp of sesame oil and sprinkle over the black sesame seeds.

Lamb Keftas

Lamb is rich in the mineral selenium, a potent antioxidant that supports detoxification and is absolutely essential for thyroid gland function and a healthy metabolic rate. This dish is full of fragrant herbs and spices: immunity-enhancing onion and garlic, and digestion-enhancing mint, parsley and coriander. In the sauce, the labneh provides probiotics to support gut health, and the tahini contains lots of calcium, essential for muscle contraction and a regular heartbeat.

 Ingredients

■ *Serves 4*

1 tsp fennel seeds
1 tsp cumin seeds
1 tsp ground coriander
1 medium onion
4 garlic cloves
1 cup (40g) flat leaf parsley
1 cup (40g) coriander leaves, plus extra for serving (1 tbsp roughly chopped)
1 cup (40g) mint leaves
3 cups (680g) lean minced lamb – if you can, buy lean cuts of lamb and mince yourself in a regular food processor
Sea salt and ground black pepper
2 tbsp raw coconut oil, plus more for grill
For the sauce
¼ cup (70g) plain whole milk yoghurt or labneh
2 tsp tahini
2 tbsp lemon juice
1 handful shredded mint leaves

 To make

1. Toast the fennel and cumin seeds in a small dry frying pan over medium-high heat for about 1 minute. Keep them moving until fragrant. Cool, then coarsely grind in a pestle and mortar (or grind in a blender). Transfer to a food processor and add the ground coriander.
2. Roughly chop the onion, garlic, parsley, coriander and mint; add to the seeds mixture and process until very finely chopped.
3. Transfer mixture to a large bowl, add minced lamb and season with salt and pepper. Using your hands, gently mix together until evenly combined. Chill mixture in the fridge for an hour, or as long as you have. This mixture can be made up to a day ahead and kept chilled or frozen.
4. Heat the grill or griddle pan to a medium-high heat and brush with a little coconut oil. Divide lamb mixture into 8 portions. Form each portion into a 10–15cm-long sausage shape. Insert a skewer lengthwise through each "sausage". Melt coconut oil in a pan and drizzle keftas with the oil and grill, turning occasionally, until just cooked through: 8–10 minutes.
5. Meanwhile, in a small bowl, mix together the yoghurt, tahini, lemon juice and shredded mint leaves, until smooth. Season with salt and pepper.
6. Serve the keftas with the sauce, extra coriander leaves, lemon wedges and warm Gluten-Free Flatbreads (*see p. 101*), Tabbouleh with a Twist (*see p. 113*) or Sweet and Sour Slaw (*see p. 111*).

Gluten-Free Flatbreads

These gluten-free and wheat-free flatbreads are a great option for those who are sensitive to wheat and gluten products. It means most people can enjoy them without the bloating or discomfort that processed wheat flatbreads can cause.

This recipe is also higher in protein than flatbreads made with white wheat flour, so they will help you feel fuller for longer.

 ## Ingredients

■ *Serves 8*

½ cup (80g) chickpea (gram) flour
½ cup (70g) rice flour
1 cup (120g) tapioca flour
2 tsp cumin seeds
1 tsp sea salt
4 tbsp coconut oil, melted
2 egg whites, lightly whisked with a fork

 ## To make

1. Measure out the flours by dipping the measuring cup into the flour and scraping the top with a knife. Place the chickpea flour, rice flour, tapioca flour and sea salt into a medium-sized mixing bowl. Stir together until well combined. Sprinkle in the cumin seeds.
2. Melt the coconut oil and add to the flour mixture, and stir until incorporated (mixture will be lumpy and fairly dry).
3. Add the egg whites and stir until well combined.
4. Transfer the dough to a cutting board or flat surface and knead for about 1 minute; the dough should be moist but not sticky. If dough is too wet, add a little more flour. If too dry, add a little more water, ½ tsp at a time.
5. Place a large shallow frying pan over medium-high heat.
6. Separate the dough into 8 pieces, knead each piece for about 30 seconds, then roll into a ball and place in the mixing bowl. When not in use, keep the dough covered with a clean dish towel.
7. Place a dough ball between 2 pieces of baking parchment and flatten with a rolling pin. Fold in half and then half again, roll out again – this adds layers and pockets of air to the dough. A finished flatbread should be about 15cm in diameter.
8. Place one flatbread in the hot pan and cook until small bubbles appear across the surface – about 30–60 seconds. Flip the flatbread over and cook the other side for another 30–60 seconds. Don't overcook; you want the flatbread to be soft, with small, golden brown spots on the surface.
9. Transfer the cooked flatbread to a warm oven (150°C) and cover with foil or baking parchment, then continue rolling out and cooking the remaining dough.
10. Serve whole with Lamb Keftas (see p. 98) and Sweet and Sour Slaw (see p. 111), or cut (into lengths or wedges) and dip into hummus or guacamole.

Cumin and Coriander Crusted Lamb

This succulent lamb dish is a fantastic source of protein, vitamin B12 for mental function and memory and the antioxidant mineral zinc, which is essential for proper immune function and for bolstering resistance to infection. Zinc is also essential for skin healing and healthy hair.

The bone broth is mineral rich and the coriander and cumin seeds have traditionally been used to soothe and support the digestive system. It is believed that one of the ways cumin seed does this is by stimulating the production of the digestive enzymes that help to break down food.

 Ingredients

■ *Serves 2*

1 tsp cumin seeds
1 tsp coriander seeds
½ tsp black peppercorns
½ tsp sea salt
1 loin of lamb (300g), boned and rolled
1 small banana shallot (or onion)
1 garlic clove
1 tbsp chopped mint leaves
2 tbsp raw coconut oil
1 tsp tamarind paste
1 cup (250ml) lamb or chicken stock, or bone broth
2 tsp pomegranate molasses or raw honey
A pinch of ground cinnamon
Salt and black pepper to taste

 To make

1. Crush the cumin, coriander, black peppercorns and salt in a pestle and mortar. Spread onto a plate and roll the lamb loin in the mix until coated all over.
2. Finely chop the shallots (or onion) and garlic and add to a medium-sized, non-stick frying pan with the chopped mint and 1 tbsp of the coconut oil. Allow to soften for 2–3 minutes.
3. Mix the tamarind with a tablespoon of hot water and add to the pan with the stock, pomegranate molasses and cinnamon. Cook on medium heat until the sauce just starts to boil, then turn down the heat and leave to simmer. Set the oven to 180°C.
4. Whilst the sauce is simmering, heat the rest of the coconut oil in a heavy-based frying pan. Bring to a moderately high heat, then add the spice crusted lamb. Using tongs to handle the meat, sear it for about a minute on each side until it gets a nice brown crust all over. Then transfer to a small roasting tray and place in the oven to finish cooking for 20–30 minutes.
5. After simmering on a low heat for 10 minutes, pass the sauce through a sieve and into a small saucepan. Season with salt and black pepper and continue to simmer gently on a very low heat until the sauce has reduced and thickened.
6. Remove the lamb from the oven and leave to rest for 5 minutes before slicing. Arrange on the plate and spoon over the reduced sauce.
7. Serve with Kale with Sesame *(see p. 105)* and Roast Pumpkin Puree *(see p. 104)* and Spiced Cauliflower Couscous with Pomegranate *(see p. 108)* for a main meal, or with a salad dish such as Tabbouleh with a Twist *(see p. 113)*, or a green salad for a lighter meal.

Roast Pumpkin Puree

Pumpkins are a fantastically rich source of carotenes, vitamin C and some of the B vitamins. Their carotene content gives them a protective effect against many cancers (like other beta-carotene-rich vegetables).

Cumin has been used traditionally to benefit the digestive system and it is believed its volatile oils may stimulate digestive enzyme production, helping support the digestive system to break down food.

Live goat's yoghurt contains live beneficial probiotic bacteria that are essential for digestive health and a strong immune system.

 Ingredients

■ *Serves 4 as a side*

½ medium-sized pumpkin (or squash if you prefer), peeled
1 tbsp raw coconut oil
1 tsp paprika
1 tsp ground cumin
1 tbsp plain whole goat's yoghurt (or kefir)
Sea salt and black pepper

 To make

1.   Preheat the oven to 180°C.
2.   De-seed and slice the pumpkin.
3.   In a pan, melt the coconut oil, add paprika and cumin, and toss the pumpkin slices around in the seasoned oil to coat – about 1 minute. Spread on a baking sheet and roast in the oven for 30 minutes until soft.
4.   Put into a food processor and blend to a smooth consistency, add the goat's yoghurt or kefir, and continue to blend to a creamy puree. Season with salt and black pepper.

Kale with Sesame

This nutritious side dish is absolutely packed with kale and so is extremely rich in vitamin C to help support growth and repair of tissues such as the skin. It is a great source of B6, an important B vitamin that helps the body make antibodies to fight disease and helps keep blood sugar within normal ranges. Kale is also extremely rich in carotenes so has anti-cancer properties and is a good source of calcium and iron for healthy bones and blood.

The sesame seeds boost the calcium content of this dish even further, making it a great choice for people who want to look after their bones and take proactive steps to guard against osteoporosis

 ## Ingredients

■ *Serves 4 as a side*

3 cups (100g) kale – washed and chopped into 1cm strips
2 tsp toasted sesame oil
2 tsp pomegranate molasses (or raw honey)
1 tbsp white toasted sesame seeds

 ## To make

1. Heat a large, lidded non-stick pan and add the washed kale, placing the lid on straight away. Let the kale steam in the residual water for a minute – add a tablespoon or two of water to the pan if it starts to dry. Steam for 2–3 minutes until tender.
2. Remove from the heat and add sesame oil, pomegranate molasses and toasted white sesame seeds. Replace the lid and shake the pan to coat the kale. Serve and enjoy!

Creamy Mustard Dressing

This dressing will work with lots of different salads. If you want to use it as a dip for crudités, leave as a slightly thicker consistency. If you are using it to dress vegetable salads, make it on the runny side.

 ## Ingredients

■ *Serves 2*

1 tbsp raw cashew nut butter
2 tsp Dijon mustard (or mustard of your choice)
2 tsp lemon juice
1 tsp apple cider vinegar or lemon juice
Sea salt and ground black pepper
1 tsp raw honey

 ## To make

1. Mix the nut butter with the mustard.
2. Add lemon juice or vinegar and mix.
3. Season with a pinch of sea salt and black pepper.
4. In a separate bowl, mix the honey with 2 tsp of warm water and stir into the nut paste mix.
5. Add 1 tsp of water at a time until the mix just runs off the spoon when you hold it up. It shouldn't be too thin or it will lose its flavour.

Moroccan Chicken with Preserved Lemons and Olives

This chicken dish is a good source of protein and B vitamins and the amino acid cysteine. Traditionally, chicken and homemade chicken stock have been used for colds and flu to help to break up and eliminate mucus from the body. Chicken stock is rich in minerals in an easy-to-absorb form and it also contains collagen, glycine and glutamine for healthy cartilage and joints. Collagen also helps keep skin plump and young looking. Preserved lemons provide limonene, a phytochemical that shows promising anti-cancer effects; onions are antibacterial; ginger is anti-inflammatory; the coriander leaves are a digestive aid and green olives provide healthy monounsaturated fats.

 Ingredients

■ *Serves 4*

¾ tsp saffron threads, crushed, or 1.3cm (7g) fresh turmeric root, peeled and grated
⅔ cup (160ml) chicken stock, warmed
2 onions
2 garlic cloves
4 small preserved lemons (or 2 large)
1 handful each of coriander leaves and flat leaf parsley
1 tsp black peppercorns
2 tbsp raw coconut oil
1 tsp ground ginger
1 tsp ground cumin
½ tsp ground allspice (pimento)
4 chicken thighs and 4 chicken drumsticks
⅓ cup (65g) green olives

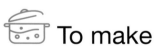 To make

1. Add the saffron threads to the stock to infuse.
2. Meanwhile, chop the onions, garlic, preserved lemons, coriander and parsley, and using a pestle and mortar (or bowl), lightly crush the black peppercorns.
3. In a tagine or heavy-bottomed lidded casserole dish, heat the oil and fry the onions until soft, then add the ginger, cumin, allspice and garlic. Cook gently for a couple of minutes.
4. Add the chicken and stir to coat with the onion and spices. Add the crushed peppercorns, preserved lemon and saffron-infused stock.
5. Bring to a simmer, then cover and cook on a very gentle heat for about 1 hour, or until the chicken is falling apart.
6. Add the olives and continue to simmer for another 10 minutes.
7. Just before serving, add the chopped coriander and parsley and then ladle into bowls.
8. Serve with Tabbouleh with a Twist (see p. 113).

Spiced Cauliflower Couscous with Pomegranate

I absolutely adore this dish! The texture is like couscous and in the same way it can be served as an accompaniment to meat dishes, but it is totally grain free. The main ingredient is cauliflower, so it is light, easy to digest and a great gluten-free alternative to traditional couscous. The addition of the sultanas, cumin and garlic means it is beneficial for digestive health. The turmeric, shallots (or onion) and pomegranate provide plenty of quercetin and vitamin C; both are natural antihistamines, which makes this dish a great choice if you get allergic eczema, asthma or hay fever.

 Ingredients

■ *Serves 4*

1 tbsp sultanas
1 large cauliflower
2 shallots (or 1 onion)
3 garlic cloves
1 tbsp raw coconut oil
2 tsp cumin seeds
2–3 tsp turmeric powder
Juice of ½ lemon
1 tbsp olive oil
Sea salt and ground black pepper
1 tbsp finely chopped flat leaf parsley
To garnish:
1 tbsp toasted pistachio nuts
Seeds of ½ pomegranate

 To make

1. Place the sultanas in a small bowl, cover in warm water and leave to soak.
2. Cut the cauliflower into equal-sized florets and steam for 4–5 minutes, until just tender, but not soft – you should be able to pierce with a fork easily. It is important not to overcook the cauliflower; you need to retain some firmness to get the right texture otherwise it will turn to mush.
3. Put the steamed cauliflower into a food processor and pulse until it resembles small grains of couscous. Roughly chop the shallots (or onions) and garlic.
4. Heat the coconut oil in a pan and add the shallots (or onions), garlic and cumin seeds. Sauté until clear, then add the turmeric and cook for 1–2 minutes more. If it is really dry (sticking to the pan), add 1 tsp more of coconut oil. Take off the heat and set aside.
5. In a warm serving dish, combine the cauliflower with the shallot mix, until the cauliflower takes on the golden turmeric colour. Squeeze in the juice of ½ lemon, and add olive oil, salt and pepper to taste.
6. Drain the soaked sultanas and stir into the cauliflower and shallot mix with the chopped parsley.
7. Serve warm or at room temperature. Sprinkle with the toasted pistachio and pomegranate to garnish.

Variations

1. If you want to turn this into a filling salad for lunch, add some shredded roast chicken and green leaves such as rocket or watercress. Dress with a tablespoon of cold-pressed virgin olive or avocado oil.
2. For a main meal, serve with the Moroccan Chicken with Preserved Lemons and Olives (*see p. 106*) or the Cumin and Coriander Crusted Lamb (*see p. 102*).

Sweet and Sour Slaw

A healthy, nutrient-packed salad. The white cabbage is full of potent, anti-cancer glucosinolates, which help the body detoxify and eliminate harmful chemicals and hormones. The antioxidant vitamin C and the amino acid glutamine help to heal and regenerate the cells of the gastrointestinal tract. The fennel contains plenty of vitamin C and is used to help relieve gas and stomach cramps and the red pigment in apples contains anthocyanidins, a type of antioxidant with many benefits including the suppression of cancer cell proliferation. Apples also contain quercetin, which helps prevent cells releasing histamine. The creamy dressing is made using cashew nuts, so it is dairy free.

Ingredients

■ *Makes 2 large salads or 4 sides*

1 tbsp chopped pecans
1 tsp nigella seeds (also known as black cumin or kalonji)
1 tsp cumin seeds
½ white cabbage
1 red apple
1 fennel bulb
1 tbsp sultanas, soaked in apple cider vinegar

To make

1. Toast the pecans, nigella and cumin seeds in a dry pan over medium heat for 1–2 minutes.
2. Finely slice the cabbage, apple and fennel and mix together with the sultanas in a bowl.
3. Add 1–2 spoonfuls of the creamy mustard dressing (*see p. 105*) and toss everything together with your hands. Sprinkle with the toasted pecans, nigella and cumin seeds, and serve.

Variations

To make this more of a meal, add a handful of cooked shredded chicken or smoked mackerel. Or serve as a side to a main course. For a vegetarian option, you could add feta cheese and cooked chickpeas.

Tabbouleh with a Twist

An immunity-boosting, anti-allergy and antioxidant-packed dish. This twist on the traditional Middle Eastern tabbouleh recipe contains absolutely loads of vitamin C from the parsley, lemon juice and pomegranate seeds, which make it a great option for anyone who wants better skin or to address allergy symptoms such as congested sinuses, sore throats or itchy eyes. Red onion provides even more antihistamine action, while cauliflower replaces the bulghur wheat, which gives additional benefits for digestion and the liver due to its antioxidant content and liver-detoxifying properties. I have observed that a congested or overtaxed liver is often a significant factor in allergy issues.

 Ingredients

■ *Serves 4*

½ medium-to-large cauliflower
1 small red onion
2 cups (80g) flat leaf parsley, finely chopped
¼ cup (30g) mint leaves
Seeds of ½ pomegranate
3 tbsp freshly squeezed lemon juice
3 tbsp extra virgin olive oil
Sea salt

 To make

1. Cut cauliflower into florets and place in a metal colander (or steamer) and steam over a pan of boiling water for 4–5 minutes, until just tender but not soft. It is important not to overcook it; you need to retain some firmness to get the right texture.
2. Put the steamed cauliflower into a food processor and pulse until it resembles small grains of couscous. Set aside in a large bowl.
3. Finely chop the onion, parsley and mint, add the pomegranate seeds and mix together with the cauliflower.
4. Drizzle over the lemon juice and olive oil; season with salt to taste. Mix well.
5. Serve with hummus and Gluten-Free Flatbread *(see p. 101)* or Moroccan Chicken with Preserved Lemons and Olives *(see p. 106)*.

Zingy Vegetable Salad

This antioxidant-packed, anti-ageing salad works well as a side dish to the lamb or chicken dishes. Yellow courgettes are rich in the eyesight-boosting antioxidants lutein and zeaxanthin. Beetroot is a source of betaine that helps protect cells from environmental stress and celery contains coumarins that help boost immune function through increasing white blood cells. Avocado is rich in the antioxidant vitamin E, which protects and repairs skin damage. The ginger has anti-inflammatory properties and the lime is packed with vitamin C.

 ## Ingredients

■ *Serves 4*

1 yellow courgette (or green)
1 celery stick, leaves as well
1 golden (or red) beetroot, skin removed
½ tsp ginger root, grated
Large fresh red chilli – mild variety
1 handful (15g) coriander leaves
1 small ripe Hass avocado
Juice of ½ lime
2 tbsp extra virgin olive oil
¼ tsp raw honey
Sea salt and black pepper
1 tsp cumin seeds

 ## To make

1. Using a mandoline, shave the courgette, celery and beetroot into thin ribbons and place in a large bowl.
2. Finely grate the ginger, thinly slice half the red chilli – use less if you prefer less heat – pick the leaves off the coriander and celery, and add to the bowl.
3. Add peeled and sliced avocado.
4. To make the dressing, put the lime juice into a small bowl, add the olive oil and mix in the raw honey until combined.
5. Pour over the salad, season with salt and black pepper and toss salad.
6. To finish, toast the cumin seeds for 1–2 minutes in a small dry frying pan and sprinkle over the salad.

Roast Mackerel or Sea Bream in Spiced Butter

This light but filling fish dish is a great option for a healthy lunch or light dinner. Mackerel is an oily fish, rich in beneficial EPA and DHA, cardio-protective omega-3 oils that help to reduce cholesterol and keep blood vessels elastic. It also contains vitamin D for immunity and healthy bones.

If you choose to use sea bream, it is rich in iron and B vitamins. The lime and spices – cumin, coriander, ginger and cayenne – have digestion-enhancing and metabolism-boosting properties. They also have antibacterial actions to support the body's ability to fight infection.

 ## Ingredients

■ *Serves 2 for a light lunch or 1 for a main meal*

½ tsp sea salt
½ tsp black pepper
1 tsp cumin seeds
1 tsp coriander seeds
1–2 tsp coconut oil (depending on the size of fish)
1 whole mackerel or sea bream (gutted, cleaned and descaled)
½ tsp cayenne pepper
½ tsp ground ginger
4 curry leaves
1 lime, sliced
A few slices of fresh ginger root

 ## To make

1. Preheat the oven to 180°C.
2. Put the salt, pepper, cumin and coriander seeds into a pestle and mortar, or spice grinder, and grind into a fine powder.
3. Melt the coconut oil in a small pan on the stove top or in a small ramekin in the oven for a few minutes.
4. Add all of the spices (including the cayenne and ground ginger) to the melted oil.
5. Pat the fish dry with paper towel and place it on baking parchment on a baking tray.
6. Place the curry leaves, lime and ginger slices inside the fish.
7. Spoon half the spiced oil over the fish, spread evenly, turn over and repeat on the other side.
8. Place in a preheated oven for 20 minutes if using mackerel, or at least 30 minutes if using a large sea bream. Check at the end of the cooking time: using a sharp knife, lift a little flesh from close to the bone – it should be opaque.
9. Remove from oven and leave the fish to rest for 5 minutes to finish cooking.
10. Serve with fresh steamed asparagus or a fresh green salad, or the Sweet and Sour Slaw (*see p. 111*).

Tamarind Roasted Red Snapper

This dish works equally well for lunch or for dinner. Red snapper is a great source of lean protein but if you can't find sustainably sourced snapper, substitute it with sea bass. The cashew nut butter provides copper, essential for energy production and repair of connective tissues; the mineral magnesium, vital for bone health; and zinc to help you fight infections. Tamarind, which has traditionally been used to aid digestion and help people with blood sugar and weight issues, provides a tangy yet sweet flavour to the dish. It also provides additional magnesium, a mineral that is important for helping alleviate anxiety, and iron for red blood cell production. The anchovies provide metabolism-enhancing and skin-boosting omega-3 fatty acids. These fats are anti-inflammatory and eating them may lead to smoother, younger looking skin.

 Ingredients

■ *Serves 2*

1 red snapper fillet (600g), skinned
¼ tsp black peppercorns
1.3cm long (7g) piece ginger root, grated
½ red or green chilli, finely chopped
1 garlic clove, chopped
2 anchovies
1 tbsp cashew nut butter – preferably raw
2 tsp tamarind paste
Juice of ½ lime

 To make

1. Preheat the oven to 180°C.
2. Pat the fish dry with paper towel.
3. In a pestle and mortar, crush the black peppercorns, ginger, chilli, garlic and anchovies to a paste.
4. Transfer to a small bowl and mix in the cashew nut butter, tamarind and lime juice. Mix thoroughly to combine everything.
5. Spread the paste all over the fish fillet, covering thoroughly.
6. Place on a shallow roasting tray and roast in the oven for 10–12 minutes until cooked. If the fillets are on the bone, they will take a little longer. Check after 8 minutes with a sharp pointed knife – poke into the flesh and see if the flesh separates easily and is opaque through to the centre.
7. Serve with Zingy Vegetable Salad (*see p. 115*), some fresh steamed greens or a green salad.

Barley Risotto with Preserved Lemons and Olives

This deliciously creamy risotto is made with pearl barley rather than risotto rice, because as a whole grain it is more nutritious and richer in soluble fibre. It works well as a meal in itself, or can be served as an accompaniment to one of the meat or fish dishes.

The banana shallot (a type of onion) is very rich in vitamin C, vitamin B6 and biotin, which is a B vitamin needed for healthy skin and hair. Studies have shown that onions have the ability to significantly lower blood sugar, which can be helpful for some diabetics and may be beneficial to people with asthma as they help prevent bronchial muscle spasm. The preserved lemons provide extra vitamin C and the dates are full of fibre for digestive health. The pine nuts contain vitamins B1 and B3, manganese and zinc.

If you add clams, which are one of the richest food sources of iron, you will boost the iron content of this dish.

 ## Ingredients

■ *Serves 2 as a main meal or 4 as a side dish*

1 banana shallot or onion, finely chopped
2 tsp raw coconut oil
2 garlic cloves, crushed and chopped
1 cup (150g) pearl barley
1 cup (250ml) verjuice (unfermented grape juice) or water
4 cups (1 litre) of vegetable or chicken stock
1 small preserved lemon, chopped into 1cm cubes
3 anchovies, chopped
Few sprigs fresh thyme (or ½ tsp dried thyme)
¼ cup (45g) green olives (black or a mix will also work), pitted
1 tbsp dates, pitted and chopped
Sea salt and black pepper
To garnish: 1 tbsp toasted pine nuts.
1 heaped tbsp finely chopped flat leaf parsley

 ## To make

1. In a medium saucepan, sauté the shallot in the coconut oil for 2 minutes, then add the garlic and continue to sauté on a medium heat until soft and clear for about 4-5 minutes.
2. Add the barley, stir to coat with a little oil and let it warm through in the pan. Add the verjuice (if you're using it) or water, stir through and heat to a gentle simmer for 5 minutes.
3. Add the stock, lemon, anchovies and thyme, and stir through. Cover the pan and leave to cook gently on a low heat, for 30 minutes.
4. Chop half the olives and leave the rest whole.
5. After 30 minutes, stir in the olives and dates. If the mixture is getting dry, add a little water to just cover the barley. Leave to cook on a low heat for another 30 minutes – checking half way through to make sure there is enough moisture. The barley will give a lovely creamy consistency.
6. After 1 hour the barley should be cooked through. Add salt and pepper to taste.
7. Serve sprinkled with the toasted pine nuts and parsley and if serving as a main meal with some fresh green vegetables, or a green salad on the side.

Variations

Cooked fish or shellfish such as clams make a great addition to this dish as a main meal – simply stir through at the end of cooking.

Quinoa and Chickpea Salad with Artichoke and Rocket

This salad is filling but light and high in protein and iron from the quinoa and chickpeas. Quinoa is also a great source of calcium, which is important for blood clotting as blood needs to clot for wounds to stop bleeding, and is much more digestible than couscous, which is made from refined wheat that can cause bloating. Studies have shown that onions help decrease blood pressure and can also prevent blood clots. Rocket, watercress, artichoke and lemon all help the body detoxify by supporting liver clearance of harmful toxins. The vitamin C in the lemon also enhances the absorption of the non-heme iron in the quinoa and chickpeas.

Ingredients

■ *Serves 2*

1 cup (160g) red quinoa (you can also use the white/tricolour, but red is better visually)
1 tsp raw coconut oil
½ banana shallot (or onion)
1 cup (200g) grilled artichokes in oil (drained)
1 good handful (50g) rocket leaves
2 cups (450g) cooked chickpeas (use canned or cook them from dry yourself)
1 tbsp cold-pressed olive oil (plus 1 tsp extra to drizzle over the haloumi)
1 tsp lemon juice
1 tsp raw apple cider vinegar
Sea salt and ground black pepper
4 slices haloumi cheese (optional – you can leave this out if dairy intolerant)
1 tsp pomegranate molasses (or honey)
To garnish: seeds of ½ pomegranate

For the avocado dressing
½ ripe avocado
1 generous handful (20g) each of coriander and watercress leaves
2 garlic cloves
¼ cup (25g) raw pine nuts
3 preserved anchovies
Juice of 1 lemon

 # To make

1. Place the quinoa in a saucepan with 1 tsp of coconut oil over medium-high heat. Melt the oil and stir through the quinoa to give all the grains a good coating (they will look glossy).
2. Continue to stir over the heat until the grains start to pop, then add 2 cups of water (twice the volume of the quinoa). Bring to a boil, then turn the heat down to a low simmer and cover the pan. Leave to cook for 10 minutes.
3. Whilst the quinoa is cooking, finely chop the shallot, quarter the artichokes and rinse and dry the rocket.
4. After 10 minutes, most of the water should have been absorbed from the quinoa and little steam holes formed on the top. Take off the heat, replace the lid and leave to finish cooking in the pan whilst you prepare the dressing.
5. Place all of the ingredients for the dressing into a blender and blend to a smooth consistency. Taste to check if salt is needed – the anchovies will provide a reasonable amount and you don't want to over-salt.
6. If the dressing is a little thick, add a little more lemon juice or a tablespoon of water – any more will dilute the flavour.
7. Put the quinoa into a salad bowl and add the cooked chickpeas, artichokes, rocket and shallots; stir to mix. Then stir in the olive oil, lemon juice and apple cider vinegar. Season to taste with salt and pepper.
8. Drizzle the haloumi with the extra teaspoon of olive oil and the pomegranate molasses and sear on a hot griddle pan, turning once.
9. Top the salad with the haloumi, sprinkle with the pomegranate seeds and drizzle over the dressing.

Snacks and Treats

Almond Cake with Apricots and Cardamom

I absolutely love this rich, spicy, moist cake! It is protein rich from all the nuts, seeds and eggs which make it very nourishing – you only need a little to feel satisfied. Almonds are one of the richest food sources of calming magnesium and the chia seeds and the spices – cardamom, saffron and cinnamon – enhance digestion. Coconut cream contains weight loss-enhancing fats, as well as iron for red blood cell production and strong nails and hair. There are more metabolism-enhancing benefits from the coconut oil and, instead of using refined sugar, the cake is sweetened with coconut blossom sugar, dates and dried apricots, which are rich in fibre and minerals.

Ingredients

■ *Serves 8*

¾ cup (175ml) good quality coffee
½ tsp saffron threads
1 cup (140g) pitted dates
2 cups (275g) gluten-free flour (for example, a mix of ¾ chestnut flour and ¼ rice flour)
1 cup (130g) ground almonds
3 tsp baking powder
1 tsp ground cinnamon
¼ tsp sea salt
1 tbsp chia seeds
1 tsp cardamom pods
6 eggs
½ cup (85g) coconut blossom sugar
1 cup (140g) melted, lukewarm coconut oil
2 tbsp coconut cream, grated (or ¼ cup/60ml coconut milk)
1 cup (250g) dried apricots
To garnish:
A drizzle of raw honey
A handful of flaked toasted almonds

To make

1. Preheat the oven to 170°C. Grease a 20cm baking tin for a large cake – you can use either a square or round tin.
2. Make a triple espresso (¾ cup/175ml of coffee or use Cold Brew Coffee (*see p. 59*) and put the saffron threads in to soak.
3. Put the dates and flour into a food processor and blend until the dates have ground down. The flour stops the dates sticking together.
4. Place the date and flour mix in a medium bowl with the ground almonds, baking powder, cinnamon and salt, and set aside.
5. In a pestle and mortar (or grinder), grind the chia seeds and cardamom pods. Add these to the coffee and saffron mix to soak.
6. Separate the egg whites and yolks into two clean bowls. Lightly beat the egg yolks until just broken up and add coconut sugar, coconut oil, coffee and saffron mix and coconut cream (or coconut milk), one item at a time, mixing between each addition until combined into a creamy mixture.
7. Whisk the egg whites in a separate bowl until they form soft peaks. This will add air to the mix and help the cake to rise.
8. Split the dried apricots in half and open out. Lay them over the bottom of the cake tin sticky side up.
9. Fold the flour mixture into the egg yolk mix 1 cup at a time, stirring lightly until just blended.
10. Fold in ⅓ of the egg whites, working quickly to mix thoroughly. Then fold the rest through gently to retain as much air as possible.
11. Pour the mixture into the apricot-lined tin and distribute evenly. Bake for 45–55 minutes until a skewer inserted in the middle comes out clean.
12. Let the cake cool for 30 minutes before removing from the tin. Drizzle over the raw honey while the cake is warm and sprinkle over the toasted almonds.

Labneh with Toasted Almonds and Lavender Honey

A super-light and deliciously creamy dessert, the probiotic-rich labneh is good for enhancing digestive health and contains beneficial bacteria to boost immunity and support healthy hormone balance. The almonds provide relaxing and calming magnesium and the propolis in the raw honey has anti-viral and anti-bacterial qualities, providing more immune support. The dried lavender flowers have calming and relaxing properties that can help to reduce anxiety. Raspberries are low in natural sugars, which makes them a great choice of fruit for diabetics and also a good source of cancer-fighting ellagic acid.

 Ingredients

■ *Serves 2*

½ cup (250g) plain labneh
1 heaped tbsp flaked almonds
2 tsp raw honey
2 tsp cold-pressed argan oil (or other good quality oil such as olive, walnut or avocado)
2 drops lavender oil (must be pure food grade oil) or you can use ½ tsp of dried lavender flowers
To decorate:
Dried lavender flowers (or dried rose petals)
A handful of fresh raspberries

 To make

1. Put the labneh into a muslin bag or fine sieve and rest over a bowl in the fridge for 1–2 hours. This will drain the excess liquid and firm up the labneh.
2. Put the almonds in a heavy-based pan and toast on medium heat, tossing frequently to cook evenly and to make sure they don't burn.
3. Remove the strained labneh from the fridge, discarding any liquid in the bowl. If you are using lavender flowers instead of lavender oil, mix these into the labneh.
4. Roll or shape the labneh into a sausage or terrine shape about 20cm long and 5cm wide, and place in the centre of a serving dish.
5. In a small bowl, mix together the honey, argan oil and, if using, the lavender oil. Place the bowl over a pan of hot water if it is a little reluctant to blend.
6. Once cooled, sprinkle the almonds all over, patting around the sides to give the labneh a nut crust. If firm enough, you can also roll the labneh in the almonds.
7. Sprinkle over the lavender buds, or rose petals, and fresh raspberries to decorate.
8. Drizzle the honey and oil mixture over the labneh and enjoy.

Billionaire's Bites

These little beauties are rich, sweet and absolutely heavenly! They are a deliciously decadent treat packed full of goodness and are really satisfying – so you don't need much. They are filled with tons of different nuts, especially pistachios, which contain a compound called oleanolic acid that studies suggest can help relieve inflammatory skin conditions such as eczema and acne.

The mineral-rich dates, vitamin C-rich goji berries and beta-carotene-packed dried apricots are all skin supportive, enhancing skin regeneration and radiance. The raw, dark chocolate provides lots of anti-ageing antioxidants.

 ## Ingredients

■ *Makes approx 20 pieces*

3–4 tbsp dried apricots
2–3 drops sweet orange essential oil (food grade)
¼ cup (30g) each of almonds, Brazil nuts, walnuts and cashew nuts
½ cup (60g) dates
⅓ cup (50g) goji berries
½ tsp ground cinnamon
½ tsp ground cardamom
1.3cm long (7g) piece ginger root, finely grated
1 tbsp each of melted cacao butter and coconut oil (or 2 tbsp coconut oil)
1 tbsp coconut flour
1 cup (150g) pistachio nuts (roasted in the oven for 10 minutes at 180°C)
½ cup (50g) dark, raw, organic chocolate to decorate (min 70% cacao)[1]

 ## To make

1. Line a 20x20cm and 2.5cm deep baking tray with baking parchment leaving some poking out above the sides of the tray to use as handles.
2. Put the apricots into a bowl with a few tablespoons of warm water and the orange oil. Leave to soak.
3. Put all the nuts, except pistachios, in a blender with the dates, goji berries, cinnamon, cardamom and grated ginger. Blitz until it forms a sticky, rough paste. It should hold together when you pinch a little with your fingers.
4. Add the melted cacao butter and coconut oils, followed by the coconut flour and pulse in the blender to combine.
5. Empty the mixture out into the lined baking tray and press down firmly to form an even base. It should be quite firm, compact and level. Place in the fridge to chill for 10–15 minutes.
6. Melt the chocolate in a glass bowl over a pan of just boiled water.
7. Slice the apricots into strips and roughly chop the pistachios.
8. Remove the base from the fridge and scatter over the sliced apricots, pressing down a little to get an even layer.
9. Sprinkle over the chopped pistachio nuts to cover evenly, and then drizzle over the melted chocolate in a criss-cross pattern to finish. Put back in the fridge for 20–30 minutes until the chocolate is set.
10. Remove from the tray using the baking parchment paper handles and place on a chopping board. Cut into 2.5cm squares. Store in the fridge in an airtight container for up to a month.

[1] *To make your own: melt 25g raw cacao butter in a bowl over some just boiled water; add 20g of raw cacao powder, 5g coconut blossom sugar or 1 tbsp date syrup.*

Cacao and Goji Nutty Bars

Another popular, deliciously sweet, crunchy and nourishing treat. These bars are really versatile, too, and can be enjoyed with tea or coffee at home with friends and family, or eaten as a light breakfast or snack on the go. They are full of fibre-rich oats and cacao butter, which contain oleic acid and polyphenols with anti-inflammatory properties, and are rich in protein-packed nuts and seeds and antioxidant-packed goji berries. The dates contain at least 15 minerals, including antioxidant, thyroid-boosting and metabolism-enhancing selenium. The raw cacao nibs boost feel-good endorphins.

 Ingredients

■ *Makes 10 large bars*

1 cup (100g) cacao butter
3 tbsp raw honey
2 cups (250g) nuts and seeds (a mixture of almonds, Brazils, walnuts, pumpkin and sunflower seeds)
½ cup (60g) dates
2 cups (250g) rolled oats
¼ cup (40g) chia seeds (or sesame seeds)
⅓ cup (50g) goji berries
⅓ cup (50g) raw cacao nibs

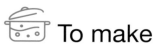 To make

1. Melt cacao butter over low heat (in a large glass bowl over a pan of boiling water). Add the honey and let dissolve into the cacao butter.
2. Put the nuts, dates and rolled oats briefly into a food processor and pulse a few times to break them down (so they are roughly chopped but not too fine).
3. Add nuts, seeds, dates, oats and all other ingredients to the melted cacao mix and stir well.
4. Line a shallow baking tray with baking parchment leaving a little bit poking above the edge of the tray to use as handles when you remove the bars. Tip the mixture into the tin whilst still warm, shake to level out and nudge to an even level. Then press the mixture down firmly, levelling the top. It is a good idea to put another sheet of baking parchment over the top, so that you don't get the mixture all over your hands.
5. Chill in the fridge until set.
6. Using the baking parchment as handles, lift the solid mix out of the tray and put on a flat surface to cut into bars of desired size. You should get 10 large bars out of this mix. Wrap each bar in baking parchment or waxed paper and store in the fridge. They keep for a month.

Crushed Broad Bean Dip with Flatbread

A tasty, savoury snack that is high in protein, minerals and fibre, courtesy of the broad beans and chickpeas, and healthy fats and skin-nourishing vitamin E from the avocado. It is a great low GI snack that helps keep blood sugar levels stable and appetite under control. The apple cider vinegar and lime juice enhance digestion and the thermogenic properties of the chilli boost metabolism and fat burning.

 Ingredients

- *Serves 2*

1 cup (100g) cooked broad beans (fresh or frozen)
½ ripe avocado
2 tsp olive oil
1 tbsp fresh lime juice
2 tsp apple cider vinegar
½ red chilli, finely chopped
Sea salt and ground black pepper
1 tbsp coriander leaves, chopped

 To make

1. Place all the ingredients, except the coriander, in a bowl or pestle and mortar, and mash together to form a rough mixture (or pulse in a food processor). Add the coriander and mix together to complete the chunky dip.
2. Toast a flatbread, or a slice of sourdough bread, spread with some hummus and pile the crushed broad bean and avocado mix on top.
3. Season and serve with a fresh tomato salad for a snack or light lunch.

Five-day Menu

The meals and recipes in this book have been created so that they can be eaten in any combination to provide a healthy, nutrient-rich diet – there really isn't a wrong way to eat them.

I have created this five-day example menu to give you a feel for how you can plan and combine the dishes throughout your day. If you are starting the day by going to a yoga class or the gym, then you could have a smoothie first thing and eat one of the lighter breakfasts after you have exercised (if you are hungry), or wait until lunch before you eat again.

The daily snacks are optional, so only eat them if you feel hungry between meals; a small portion of one of the treats should do the job.

Day 1

On waking: Skin Radiance Boosting Water *(see p. 59)*
Breakfast: Omelette with Feta, Rainbow Chard and Turmeric *(see p. 71)*
Lunch: Broad Bean, Fennel and Avocado Salad with Chicken *(see p. 94)*
Snack: Choco-Berry Love Potion Smoothie *(see p. 49)*
Dinner: Barley Risotto with Preserved Lemons and Olives *(see p. 120)*

Day 2

On waking: Turmeric Tea *(see p. 57)*
Breakfast: Super Berry Granola *(see p. 75)*
Lunch: Spicy Fish Broth with Fresh Greens *(see p. 96)*
Snack: One Billionaire's Bite *(see p. 130)*
Dinner: Moroccan Chicken with Lemons and Olives *(see p. 107)* and Tabbouleh with a Twist *(see p. 113)*

Day 3

On waking: Skin Radiance Boosting Water *(see p. 59)*
Breakfast: Pear and Cinnamon Pancakes *(see p. 62)*
Lunch: Beetroot and Chicory Salad with Horseradish Goat's Curd *(see p. 84)*
Snack: Skin Renew Juice *(see p. 55)*
Dinner: Tamarind Roasted Red Snapper *(see p. 119)* with Zingy Vegetable Salad *(see p. 115)*

Day 4

On waking: Super Green Detox Juice *(see p. 55)*
Breakfast: Asparagus Frittata *(see p. 64)*
Lunch: Chicory, Fennel and Apple Salad with Hot Smoked Salmon *(see p. 86)*
Snack: Crushed Broad Bean Dip with Flatbread *(see p. 135)*
Dinner: Cumin and Coriander Crusted Lamb *(see p. 102)* with Spiced Cauliflower Couscous with Pomegranate *(see p. 108)*

Day 5

On waking: Skin Radiance Boosting Water *(see p. 59)*
Breakfast: Bircher Muesli with Passion Fruit and Coconut *(see p. 69)*
Lunch: Quinoa and Chickpea Salad with Artichoke and Rocket *(see p. 122)*
Snack: Creamy Vanilla Berry Smoothie *(see p. 51)*
Dinner: Velvet Mushroom Soup *(see p. 80)*

Wholesome Foods Ingredient Guide

There is no doubt that we benefit greatly from eating more nutrient-dense foods with health-enhancing properties. As one of the Six Pillars of Wellness, having a wholesome diet can transform our wellness and make a huge difference to our quality of life.

The following is a list of the key wholesome foods that I have used in the recipes in this book and some of their benefits.

Adding more of these to your diet can help you reap the benefits that they provide and move towards greater personal well-being.

Fats and oils

Buy these plant oils, cold pressed in dark glass bottles: coconut, argan, avocado, extra virgin olive oil, walnut and flaxseed and choose "grass-fed", organic butter.

Coconut oil – rich in health-promoting, antimicrobial medium-chain saturated fats (special saturated fats that help fight disease-causing pathogens) while coconut flesh is a great source of minerals, including manganese, copper, selenium and zinc. Great for strengthening immunity!

Argan oil – cold-pressed oil from the kernels of the Moroccan argan tree, rich in fatty acids, which have been shown to improve insulin sensitivity and may help in the prevention of obesity and type 2 diabetes. It also contains vitamin E for a healthy immune system.

Avocado oil – rich in antioxidant and anti-ageing vitamin E to nourish the skin, and in oleic and linoleic acid, both oils that can help lower cholesterol.

Extra virgin olive oil – made from crushed and pressed olives. Extra virgin refers to the unrefined oil from the first crushing of the olives and has the most health benefits. Olive oil is rich in antioxidants, has anti-inflammatory properties and may also be helpful in the prevention and treatment of asthma, arthritis, breast cancer and diabetes.

“ Natural butter, from grass-fed cows, is much healthier than manufactured margarine and is packed with vitamins A, D, E and K...”

Walnut oil –rich in the antioxidant ellagic acid. This antioxidant has the ability to protect cells from free-radical damage and helps to prevent cancer cells from multiplying. Walnuts contain the highest amount of a type of omega-3 oil called alpha linolenic acid (ALA), an oil that supports healthy cell membranes and the development of the brain, retina and eyes in the foetus, so is particularly important for pregnant women.

Butter – natural butter, from grass-fed cows, is much healthier than manufactured margarine and is packed with vitamins A, D, E and K, a range of minerals and healthy immunity-boosting fats with antimicrobial properties. If your butter is sourced from cows that feed on green grass it can also contain high levels of conjugated linoleic acid (CLA), a compound that may help provide protection against cancer. It has also been shown to help the body maintain muscle mass and decrease fat during weight loss programs.

Flaxseed oil – made from the seeds of the flax plant. This oil is an excellent source of the omega-3 essential fatty acid alpha-linolenic acid (ALA), which has been shown to have many health benefits, including reducing cancer risk, and may actually help to shrink breast tumours. It can also be helpful in improving skin conditions such as eczema. Always buy it cold pressed; it needs to be refrigerated and shouldn't be used for cooking as heat damages it. So add it to dishes after cooking and use it in dressings, marinades or smoothies.

Superfoods

Superfoods are nutrient-dense foods that are particularly rich in compounds that are beneficial to health such as antioxidants, fatty acids and fibre. Some have been used therapeutically for thousands of years to treat and prevent disease.

Chia seeds – these nutrient-packed little seeds from Central and South America contain lots of ALA. High in protein and fibre, they help promote bowel regularity and may help you feel fuller for longer and are very high in protective antioxidants. They have been shown to help maintain balanced blood fats, have beneficial effects on cholesterol levels and help reduce inflammation in the body (inflammation contributes to the development of heart disease and many other health conditions).

" Maca ... has been used as a medicinal plant for thousands of years. Traditionally it has been used to increase energy, strength and endurance."

Maca – the powdered root of a Peruvian plant that grows in the Andes that has been used as a medicinal plant for thousands of years. Traditionally it has been used to increase energy, stamina, strength and endurance and to address hormonal disorders. It is extremely rich in calcium, contains lots of fibre and protein and has the ability to regulate and support the hormonal system. With my clients I have seen that it can be beneficial for women with PMS, or those who are going through menopause. But one of the great things about Peruvian maca root is that it is not "gender specific" and works equally well for both men and women. However, please note that maca should be avoided during pregnancy and breastfeeding as it has hormone-modulating properties.

Lucuma powder – a light yellow powder made from ground lucuma fruit, which is known in Peru as the "Gold of the Incas". It is a great low glycaemic index (GI) alternative sweetener because it provides a sweet, unique flavour to foods without causing a big spike in blood sugar levels. Rich in minerals, iron (needed for red blood cell production and oxygenation of the brain and body) and vitamins, including beta-carotene, an anti-ageing antioxidant that rejuvenates and heals the skin, the nutrients in lucuma are also great for boosting eyesight, energy and endurance.

Goji berries – grown in China, India and Tibet, these little red, antioxidant-packed, super berries contain polysaccharides, a type of sugar that boosts white blood cell production and helps to enhance immunity. Its antioxidants include lutein, which improves eye health and protects the eyes from damage.

Vanilla powder – the ancient Mayans believed that vanilla drinks had energising properties and this sweet-flavoured, fragrant brown powder is made from pure, raw ground vanilla pods. It contains small amounts of minerals and the B-complex vitamins that help nervous system function, provide energy and regulate the body's metabolism.

Matcha green tea powder – is a special powdered green tea made from nutrient-rich young leaves picked from the tips of Camellia sinensis plants grown in the shade to increase the chlorophyll content. Antioxidant packed, it has one of the highest antioxidant levels of any food or drink. It is particularly rich in a type of antioxidant known as catechins that helps halt oxidative damage to cells. Studies have found an association between consuming green tea and a reduced risk for several cancers, including skin, breast, lung, colon, oesophageal and bladder.

Matcha also contains amino acid L-theanine, which promotes the production of alpha waves in the brain. This relaxes the mind without inducing drowsiness and helps counteract the stimulatory effects of caffeine.

L-theanine also promotes the production of dopamine, serotonin and GABA – brain chemicals that enhance mood, reduce anxiety and promote better concentration and memory.

Some studies also suggest that matcha green tea can enhance both resting metabolic rate and fat burning.

Acerola cherry powder – this orangey-red powder from a tropical fruit is extremely rich in vitamin C. It supports immunity and enhances collagen synthesis (collagen is essential for plump, younger looking skin). Vitamin C is also an antioxidant that neutralises many types of free radicals and supports capillary health.

> *Bee pollen has traditionally been used to improve the appearance of skin and nails, to ease menopausal symptoms, to alleviate nasal allergy symptoms... and to enhance energy and sports performance."*

Bee pollen – a complete protein, pollen contains all the essential amino acids, as well as B vitamins, the nucleic acids DNA and RNA, vitamin C, plant hormones and antioxidants. The ethanol extracts it contains demonstrate antimicrobial and antiviral activity and it has anti-inflammatory and anti-allergic actions – thought to be due to the presence of kaempferol and quercetin flavonoids. Bee pollen has traditionally been used to improve the appearance of skin and nails, to ease menopausal symptoms, to alleviate nasal allergy symptoms (hay fever) and to enhance energy and sports performance. Bee pollen is used by body builders and athletes to help increase lean muscle and decrease recovery time after workouts.

Chlorella – this bright green powder is a freshwater algae that is extremely nutrient dense. It contains protein, vitamins A, C, D, E, and K, B vitamins, many minerals, chlorophyll and the nucleic acids RNA and DNA. Nucleic acids are associated with healing, cellular repair and anti-ageing

Nuts and seeds

Nuts and seeds are a rich source of minerals, protein and healthy fats and a great way to super power your diet with omega-3 and zinc. They can also help to balance female hormones.

Brazil nuts – very rich in healthy, polyunsaturated fats and the richest food source of the mineral selenium, which is a potent antioxidant that reduces the risk of cancer and is essential for thyroid function. Our thyroid gland has a huge impact on our metabolic rate, and how well it functions can affect our ability to lose weight.

Cashews – rich in relaxing magnesium, energising iron and immune-boosting, skin-healing zinc. They are also rich in the fat oleic acid, a monounsaturated fat with benefits including protection against heart disease and cancer.

Walnuts – contain omega-3 fatty acid ALA and are packed full of beneficial, health-protective antioxidants, minerals and the amino acid arginine, which converts into nitrous oxide to help blood vessels relax. Walnuts also have many other benefits for the heart and cardiovascular system, including reducing cholesterol and triglycerides.

Almonds – rich in monounsaturated and polyunsaturated oils and 20% protein. They are a great source of relaxing magnesium, bone-strengthening calcium, iron, zinc, vitamin E, vitamin B2, fibre and anti-ageing antioxidants.

Sesame seeds and tahini (a paste of ground sesame seeds) – are a very rich source of calcium (1 cup of natural sesame seeds has 1404 milligrams of calcium, while 1 cup of whole milk has only 291 milligrams). Calcium is essential for healthy bones and teeth as well as for muscle contraction and heart function. The seeds also aid digestion, helping to support regular bowel movements.

Cacao – real chocolate

Cacao beans are the seed of the fruit from the Amazonian tree, Theobroma cacao. Theobroma cacao literally means "the food of the gods" – and chocolate is considered to be a food of the gods for good reason!

> *Theobroma cacao literally means 'the food of the gods' – and chocolate is considered to be a food of the gods for good reason!"*

Cacao was so highly valued in ancient Mayan and Aztec civilisations that cacao beans were used as currency in some parts of Central America. They were believed to have medicinal, nourishing and energising qualities and Mayan healers have traditionally used cacao for women's issues and after childbirth to nourish the mother, as well as for many other health problems.

Cacao powder, cacao butter and cacao nibs – cacao is a very good source of magnesium and rich in antioxidants and flavonoids, which help protect against damage to cholesterol and the lining of the arteries. It also contains substances that can support psychological well-being.

Chocolate and love – cacao contains phenylethylamine or PEA, a neurotransmitter that is released by our brains at moments of emotional euphoria, including when we experience feelings of love. This may explain the age-old connection between love and chocolate in so many cultures around the world.

Cacao also contains a chemical called anandamide (another pleasurable neurotransmitter) that makes us feel good, giving us a sense of bliss. We experience these benefits when we eat organic, raw dark chocolate. We don't get these same effects from eating commercial milk chocolate, which contains very little actual cacao and has cow's milk and lots of refined sugar added

Vegetables

Leafy greens, cruciferous and bitter green vegetables – which includes white cabbage, cauliflower, rainbow chard, Swiss chard, purple sprouting broccoli, spinach, rocket, watercress, kale, black kale (cavolo nero), artichoke and red chicory.

This group of vegetables is high in fibre and contains lots of vitamins A, C and K. They promote great skin due to their beta-carotene and vitamin C content, their folate content strengthens the nervous system and vitamin K promotes healthy bones. They are also rich in minerals such as calcium, potassium and magnesium and contain eye- health-enhancing phytonutrients.

Eating bitter food is thought to help activate the taste buds and stimulate enzyme production and bile flow, which promote digestion and nutrient absorption. The high fibre content in bitter greens also helps to eliminate waste through the digestive tract.

Bitter greens also promote natural detoxification of the liver. A healthy liver is crucial for cholesterol regulation, hormone balance, blood cleansing and fat metabolism.

Cruciferous vegetables – include cauliflower, cabbage, bok choy, broccoli, brussel sprouts, and similar green leafy vegetables. They contain compounds called glucosinolates, which are broken down into powerful, cancer-preventative substances: isothiocyanates and indoles.

Herbs and spices

Herbs and spices bring intense flavour to meals and are packed with phytonutrients and antioxidants. They also have potent medicinal effects; some herbs and spices can help reduce blood sugar levels, others act as anti-inflammatories, treat nausea and have antimicrobial actions.

Cardamom – a digestant and stimulant that helps prevent flatulence and indigestion, and can reduce bloating. Packed with antioxidants, it has traditionally been used in Ayurvedic medicine to help alleviate depression.

> " *Chilli ... contains capsaicin, a compound that stimulates digestion, increases basal metabolic rate, and is a safe and natural way to enhance fat burning.* "

Cayenne pepper or chilli – contains capsaicin, a compound that stimulates digestion, increases basal metabolic rate and is a safe and natural way to enhance fat burning. It is also a pain reliever that boosts feel-good endorphins, and is antibacterial and can kill food-borne bacteria.

Cinnamon – has been used as a medicinal agent for thousands of years. It is particularly useful for people with blood sugar problems and diabetes. One recent type 2 diabetes study showed a significant reduction of fasting blood glucose and cholesterol in just 40 days from using 1–6

Coconut

Coconut is one of the oldest food plants. It comes in many forms such as creamed coconut or coconut butter, coconut shavings, coconut cream (made by squeezing grated coconut flesh) and the thinner coconut milk (made by soaking coconut in water), raw coconut oil, coconut flour and coconut water (the slightly sweet fluid inside young green coconuts). Coconut, in its many forms, is a healthy substitute for dairy, gluten and sugar.

Coconut oil is the most highly saturated of all vegetable oils, which makes it extremely heat stable and excellent to cook with. The saturated fats it contains are very special medium-chain saturated fats called lauric and capric acid. These fats are powerfully antiviral and antibacterial and also promote weight loss. Studies suggest they actually speed up the body's metabolic rate – making coconut oil a fat that helps you lose fat! However, like anything, coconut oil should be consumed in moderation. Make sure your diet includes a variety of foods rich in different healthy fats. As well as raw coconut oil, use cold-pressed extra virgin olive oil and other sources of healthy fats such as avocados, raw nuts and seeds (and their cold-pressed oils).

Fruit

Fruit is a great source of vitamins, minerals and fibre and, as long as it is not eaten to excess (as fruit is high in natural sugar), it is an excellent, health-promoting addition to your diet.

Avocado – rich in antioxidant and immune-boosting vitamin E, energising and mood-balancing B vitamins (particularly B5, the "anti-stress" vitamin), healthy monounsaturated fats and potassium. It is great for skin, immunity and stress.

Lemons – are very alkalising and detoxifying. They provide digestive support, are packed with immunity-strengthening

and skin-boosting vitamin C and have also been shown to have antibacterial actions.

Dark red, blue and purple berries such as raspberries and blueberries – low in GI as they don't spike blood sugar as much as some other fruits due to their lower fructose and high fibre content. They are packed full of antioxidants including the antihistamine quercetin and proanthocyanidins. These antioxidants are anti-inflammatory, protective of cardiovascular health and anti-ageing, as they protect against free radicals that damage cells and contribute to the ageing process.

Passion fruit – rich in vitamin C, an antioxidant that protects from damaging free radicals, prevents premature ageing and helps to strengthen the immune system. It contains vitamin A, crucial for maintaining good vision, healthy skin, cell growth and reproduction. It also contains a decent amount of iron, eye sight-boosting antioxidants and fibre for regular bowel movements.

Ancient grains and pseudo grains

Ancient grains and pseudo grains are plants that have been hardly changed by selective breeding over centuries, even millennia. Many are naturally gluten-free and much more digestible than many modern grains, which have been extensively modified and cross bred making them less nutritious and less easily digested.

Pearl barley – milled whole barley pseudo grain. is one of the world's most ancient cultivated grains. A great source of fibre, it helps us to feel fuller, stabilises blood sugar levels and stimulates digestion and elimination. It also contains the relaxing mineral magnesium and antioxidant selenium.

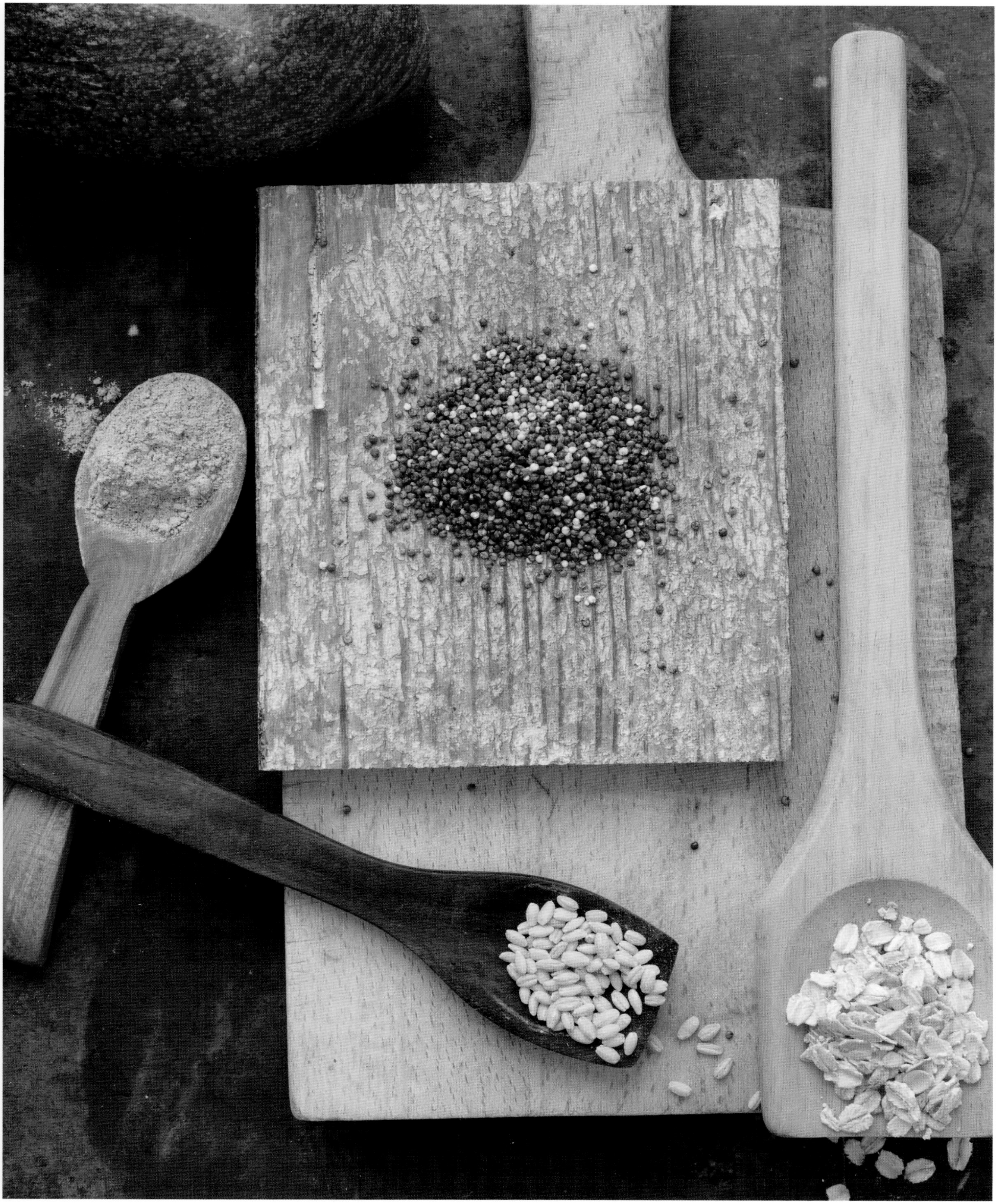

Oats – a concentrated source of fibre and nutrients, rich in minerals phosphorus, selenium, magnesium, iron and vitamin B1. Studies show that eating oats helps lower cholesterol and regulate blood sugar levels and many people find that eating fibre rich oats also helps them to go to the bathroom more regularly and easily.

Buckwheat flour – buckwheat is not a cereal grain, but actually a seed from a fruit that is rich in the flavonoid antioxidants rutin and quercetin, which are good for the cardiovascular system. Rutin helps to strengthen blood vessels, making them less likely to get damaged. Diets that contain buckwheat have been linked to a lowered risk of developing high cholesterol and high blood pressure.

Quercetin is also a natural antihistamine so it can be helpful to people with hay fever and other allergic conditions that involve histamine release, including allergic asthma. Buckwheat is rich in calming magnesium, a mineral that relaxes muscles and nourishes the nervous system, anti-stress vitamin B5 and high quality protein.

Coconut flour – made from ground and dried coconut meat. This flour is high in protein, fibre and healthy fats. It is a lower GI flour than white wheat flour (it releases its sugars more slowly), so is good for diabetics as it causes less of a spike in blood sugar levels. It is also good for those who experience digestive problems from consuming wheat as it is naturally wheat and gluten free.

Gram flour – a flour made from small chickpeas that is naturally gluten and wheat free. It contains a lot more protein and is lower in carbohydrates than wheat flour so is much better for diabetics. It is also an excellent source of folate (a B vitamin) and minerals, including iron, making it a good choice for those who want to increase their energy levels.

Tapioca flour – a flour made from the starch of the South American cassava plant that is naturally wheat and gluten free, so is low allergenic. A starchy flour used to thicken and "fluff" baked goods, it can be mixed with other alternative flours and is great to use in small amounts for baking treats and desserts.

Rice flour – naturally gluten and wheat free, this flour is made from milled brown and white rice. It contains protein, minerals and B vitamins that are essential for mood, energy production and brain function.

Chestnut flour – low in fat (chestnuts are the only low-fat nut) and rich in fibre, vitamin C and protein. It also contains B vitamins for nervous system health and energy.

Sourdough bread – sourdough bread is a slowly fermented bread that contains less gluten than other breads. Gluten is the component of grains (wheat, barley and rye) and grain products such as bread, that some people find hard to digest and that can cause bloating and constipation. Many of my clients cannot eat ordinary bread because it bloats them, but can eat sourdough bread without any problems. This is due to the fact that during the fermentation process good bacteria break down the gluten proteins, reducing or even eliminating the gluten content all together. True sourdough bread does not contain yeast and instead utilises a lactobacilli-based starter culture and is baked at a lower temperature for a longer period of time, which preserves the nutritional value of the cereal grains.

Quinoa – the least allergenic "pseudo"grain. Naturally wheat and gluten free, it is a very good source of magnesium, calcium and manganese and a very rich protein source. Quinoa is one of the few non-meat proteins that is a complete protein, which means it contains all the essential amino acids. It also contains healthy amounts of B2, vitamin E and dietary fibre and is a good source of energising iron and immune-boosting zinc.

Dairy

Natural, whole, organic dairy products, rich in beneficial probiotic bacteria can be an excellent addition to your diet and help boost gut health and immunity. However, if eating dairy causes you bloating, triggers acne, blocks your sinuses or causes other symptoms, then of course you should avoid it!

> " *Labneh ... is a cultured food, rich in beneficial probiotic bacteria that support digestive heath and so can help with digestive symptoms such as bloating.* "

Labneh (a "yoghurt cheese") – yoghurt that has been strained to remove its whey, giving it a thicker, richer, creamier consistency. It can be used in sweet or savoury recipes. The straining process means it is also lower in lactose than unstrained yoghurt. It is a cultured food, rich in beneficial probiotic bacteria that support digestive health and so can help with digestive symptoms such as bloating, hormonal imbalance (including PMS) and help to strengthen immunity – the human gut plays an important role in our immune system function.

Goat's and sheep's cheese and yoghurt – sheep's dairy is a far better source of calcium and zinc than cow dairy. Some people find goat's milk and cheese easier to digest because these have a lower lactose content and different protein structure (they also contain more calcium than dairy from cows). Live sheep's and goat's yoghurt aid digestion as they are fermented foods, rich in enzymes and friendly probiotic bacteria. They are good sources of nutrients, including the metabolism-boosting mineral potassium. Raw camel's milk is also very nutritious, with more vitamin C and more iron than cow's milk; initial studies show it also has the potential for beneficial use in diabetes management.

Kefir – can be made from the milk of cows, goats, sheep, camels and even from nut milks. Adding kefir grains to milk produces a fermented milk product like drinkable yoghurt, although "kefir grains" are actually not grains at all but a delicate balance of yeast and bacteria.

Kefir grains ferment raw milk in around 24 hours and transform the milk into a superfood probiotic drink (kefir). A naturally carbonated drink that has medicinal benefits, kefir contains high levels of vitamin B12, calcium, magnesium, vitamin K2, biotin, folate, enzymes and probiotics and can help boost immunity, support gut health and have positive effects on both allergies and asthma. You can make kefir yourself at home or buy it ready made.

Alternative sweeteners

Natural, unrefined sugars can be used to sweeten recipes and provide minerals, fibre and vitamins along with the sweetness. However, they must still be used in moderation as even natural sugars, if eaten to excess, can cause blood sugar problems.

" *Dates are one of the most alkaline foods around and also very rich in anti-cancer and antioxidant compounds.* "

Dates and raw date syrup – dates can be described as an ideal food, providing a wide range of essential nutrients and potential health benefits. They contain B vitamins and many minerals including iron and magnesium, zinc and selenium. They are a rich source of beta-D-glucan, a type of fibre that slows the absorption of sugar from the small intestine, so helping to keep blood sugar levels stable.

Beta-D-glucan also helps keep bowel movements regular. Dates are one of the most alkaline foods around and also very rich in anti-cancer and antioxidant compounds.

Coconut blossom sugar or coconut palm sugar – a natural sugar made from the dehydrated sap of the coconut plant that, unlike white table sugar, contains some trace nutrients, minerals, iron, zinc, calcium and potassium, along with some short-chain fatty acids and antioxidants. It also contains a fibre called inulin that may slow glucose absorption and explain why coconut sugar has a lower glycaemic index than refined table sugar.

Raw honey – has not been pasteurised (heat treated) or filtered and is therefore much better for you than commercially produced honey, because the natural nutritional content of the honey is preserved. Full of vitamins and minerals, including vitamins B2 and B6 and iron, antioxidant flavonoids (including some that help prevent atherosclerosis) and traces of pollen and propolis. Propolis has potent antibacterial properties and I have found it to be very useful for helping recovery from colds, flu and sore throats.

Pomegranate, quince and apple molasses – a versatile sweet and sour marinade, the juices are heated and mixed with small amounts of sugar or coconut blossom sugar and lemon juice. Pomegranates contain a higher amount of polyphenol antioxidants than most fruits and are very rich in vitamin C, so they can benefit your immune system and skin.

Dried apricots – high in fibre and a great source of potassium to help us build muscle and convert the food we eat into energy so eating more potassium-rich foods can help with weight loss. Apricots also contain iron and antioxidant carotenes, such as lycopene and lutein, which help to boost eye health and vision and prevent macular degeneration and cataracts.

Raisins and sultanas – a rich source of antioxidants such as polyphenols, which are known to reduce the risk of cardiovascular disease. Also, they contain vitamins B1 and B6 needed for concentration, memory, energy and digestion, and iron for red blood cell production and energy. High in fibre for digestive health, raisins may encourage more regular bowel movements and some people find them helpful for constipation.

Other

Raw apple cider vinegar – made by fermenting apples. Avoid the perfectly clear vinegars you see on supermarket shelves; instead choose organic, unprocessed raw apple cider vinegar that looks murky and brown. It has a cobweb-like substance floating in it, known as "mother", which is made up of strands of proteins, enzymes and friendly bacteria.

Research into raw apple cider vinegar and its benefits for blood sugar has shown increased insulin sensitivity and dramatically reduced insulin and glucose spikes occurring after meals. Therefore, it could be useful to people with type 2 diabetes and pre-diabetes as well as for maintaining healthy blood sugar levels.

It may also help you eat less. Apple cider vinegar contains lots of acetic acid and, when included in a high-carbohydrate meal, has been shown to lower the blood glucose and insulin response to food, helping to make you feel fuller. Preliminary studies indicate that it can potentially help weight loss. It is also a digestive aid that can enhance the breakdown of food and therefore help maximise nutrient absorption.

A Beautifully Balanced Life

By adopting my healthy eating principles, and by using the recipes in this book, I hope you will discover the joys of a healthier diet and a healthier you. If making these changes feels a little overwhelming at first, please don't worry. You can take things slowly, making gradual improvements to your diet.

You could start by eating more fresh vegetables; then, aim to reduce your portion sizes through mindful eating; from there, gradually cut back on the amount of refined sugar you eat. The benefits that you will start to see, and feel, from these changes will help motivate you to embrace more of the healthy habits going forward.

Equally, if you are more of an "all or nothing" person and changing many things at once works better for you, then by all means go for it! We are all different and the approach that works best for each of us will differ too.

I want you to know that your health is largely in your own hands, despite the fact that for a long time we've been led to believe that we are at the mercy of our genes. Good health overall depends very much on factors that are mostly within our control. How we eat, how we live our lives, the toxins we are exposed to, the exercise we do (or don't do), how we handle stress, even our thought processes, may all regulate gene expression and prevent, even some hereditary, diseases. Indeed, most of our genes are actually modifiable, and we change them throughout our lives with our own habits and behaviours. The food we eat and the lifestyle we lead can literally change the course of our health destiny.

So, with this in mind, I encourage you to take the knowledge you've gained from this book to make positive changes to how you eat and the way you live your life, and become an empowered creator of your own wellness and vitality.

With love
Zoë x

Index

Quality Ingredients are Key (My Food Philosophy):

  - why use organic/free range ingredients? problems with

      intensive farming (monoculture); synthetic chemical

A Beautiful Balance:
A Wellness Guide to Healthy Eating and Feeling Great

World-renowned clinical nutritionist and naturopath Zoë Palmer-Wright has over 10 years of experience as a clinician, researcher and educator and has helped thousands of people improve their health and happiness.

Whether she is working with clients one-to-one or teaching groups, Zoë aims to help people understand how food and lifestyle choices shape health and provide people with natural solutions and practical tools to get their health back on track.

Zoë Palmer-Wright